THE KAIJU SURVIVAL GUIDE

カイジュサバイバルガイド

WES PARKER

COPYRIGHT

Cover and Art Design by José Lucas at Stargazing Studio

ISBN-13: 978-1-7323272-2-1

To my wife Tiffany, I will love you for all the evers...

CONTENTS

INTRODUCTION

Kaiju

"A large strange beast, capable of great destruction"

I used to love monster movies as a kid. My brother and I would stay up late just to watch whatever monster was terrorizing the screens. Our living room floor covered in toy blocks and dinosaurs action figures. We would imitate the very same monsters we saw on tv, knocking over our building blocks as we terrorized the make-believe town's people of the living room. It was fun, or at least it was until I saw my first Kaiju up close. After that, monsters didn't seem so fun. I learned about KRSD shortly after this unfortunate experience. The Kaiju Research and Survival Department (KRSD) is the world's leading organization in the fight against the Kaiju. Their primary goal is to study the Kaiju and protect mankind in the process. A better way of explaining it is that they kick the crap out of giant monsters. I joined KRSD as a field operative (glorified reporter) almost 15 years ago. During that time, I have seen both amazing and terrifying things. I have witnessed firsthand, the destruction the Kaiju can cause and the extreme measures that human beings will go to in order to survive. The one thing that has become very apparent through my travels is that the Kaiju...are winning...

Sure, we may eliminate whatever big bad monster emerges from the depths, but not before it has already destroyed most of a city. While we understand more about the Kaiju then we did 50 years ago, we still don't know where they come from, or for that matter, what they want. Most of the time, we don't even have an indication of a Kaiju attack until it is already too late. The number of attacks has increased since the first incident in 1933, and they don't show any sign of slowing down. For that reason, my superiors at KRSD have deemed it necessary to create a survival guide for the average citizen to use against the Kaiju. For the last five years, I have overseen a 12-person team with the sole purpose of creating the survival guide before you. This has been a labor of love for many of us here at KRSD, with many members of my team having been personally affected by the Kaiju in some way. We have spent the last five years interviewing KRSD researchers, military personnel, and key survivors from every Kaiju attack on record. This guide will give you all of the known information about the Kaiju. We have included what was deemed the most important survival stories throughout the book. These stories provide a firsthand account from the victims and offer some insight for how they survived the Kaiju attacks. Every part of this guide, every word, came at an unimaginable cost. Do not discount this as the babble of a simple monster chaser. This guide and the information within might save your life one day. Only through understanding can we ever hope to defeat the Kaiju menace!

KRSD

KAIJU RESEARCH AND SURVIVAL DEPARTMENT.

WHAT IS A KAIJU?

65 million years ago, our world was owned by the dinosaurs. These giant creatures were the top of the food chain until a climate-changing event reshaped our world. This change in the environment caused many of the dinosaurs to die off. The ones that survived evolved over time, drastically changing from what they once were. This evolution was different for each species, but the one common theme was that these giants began to grow smaller. For these creatures to survive a new environment with limited resources, they had to adapt. Through this evolution—or devolution, as far as the dinosaurs are concerned—mankind emerged, and began to grow as a species and a civilization. We would certainly see traces of the giants that walked the earth, but those monsters were gone, and it was our turn to rule, or so we thought.

As humanity grew, we began to develop our own societies and cultures. Each culture would attempt to explain the unexplainable, whether it was through religion or other beliefs. The one thing they had in common, however, was that each and every one of these cultures makes some reference to Kaiju (strange beasts). We have seen examples of these beasts in our history texts, such as the Europeans and their references to dragons. The Greeks encountered multiple creatures such, as the Minotaur or Cerebus. Asian cultures have the Oni and their own variation of dragons. These creatures appear all over ancient texts with many glaring similarities, regardless of the originating culture. For a while, these creatures were thought to be a way for humanity to explain its fear of the unknown. Historians believed these monsters represented a fear of the unknown, that they were an allegory for the evils of humanity. That all changed after the events of 1933 in New York City.

The world was a strange place in 1933. The first world war had just ended 15 years earlier, the industrial revolution was coming to an end, and a second world war was on the horizon. That is why the events of 1933 often get overlooked, when in reality, they were a warning sign we should have paid more attention to. In March of 1933, a film crew returned to the United States from a year-long expedition to the rain forest. The crew left the United States with the intention of filming a nature documentary. They returned with no film, half the original crew, and a giant ape-like creature in tow. The ape itself is small by today's standard of Kaiju, but it was a modern marvel in 1933. Standing at 24 feet tall and weighing almost two tons, this creature made everyone who saw him stop and gaze in amazement. Unfortunately, this modern marvel only lasted in the States for a few days, eventually escaping captivity due to negligence on his handlers' part. The great ape was eventually put down by the military, but not before putting on quite the show of force in the city. Scientists studied the remains of the ape, but that was put on hold in 1939 when the second world war began.

War breeds desperation, and desperation breeds innovation. If anything can be said about World War Two, it's that it was one of the most destructively innovative periods of mankind. The war gave way to such inventions as jet engines, radar, programmable computers, and the Manhattan Project. The Manhattan Project was the research group that created the first nuclear bomb. One bomb has enough force to level a city, which was exactly what it was used for. In the beginning of August 1945, two nuclear bombs were dropped on the country of Japan over a period of three days. These bombs were dropped towards the end of the war, and resulted in over 200,000 deaths of military and civilian personnel. The aftereffects of the bombs plagued the country for years with radiation having lasting effects on current and future generations alike. The world had changed in more ways than one. Not only had mankind created a devastating weapon that gave them the power to wipe each other out, but as many experts now believe, these events gave birth to what is now deemed the "Modern Kaiju," which began to show up in the mid-1950s.

KAIJU ORIGINS

The modern Kaiju came alongside the 1950s. It was a period when mankind was rebuilding itself and attempting to move past the war that had taken over 60 million lives. During this period, strange reports started to come in of abnormal creatures appearing all over the globe. The beasts would be gone as fast as they appeared in most cases, with only a few sticking around long enough for someone to take a blurry photograph. These reports were mostly isolated to Japan who, in 1954, saw the first modern Kaiju. It came out of the Pacific Ocean and proceeded to terrorize the Japanese people for several days, disappearing back into the ocean after each attack. The Kaiju eventually appeared in Tokyo, where the Japan Self-Defense Forces engaged it. It was a long, brutal battle, but in the end, the Japanese were victorious. It was a time of celebration and rebuilding that unfortunately didn't last long. Just two months after this attack, a similar one took place in the United States. The Americans were able to beat the creatures, but they suffered heavy losses as well. A few months later, another Kaiju attack took place in India. Then another one happened, and another, and another, until finally, it was evident that these creatures were a problem that needed to be dealt with. Kaiju attacks have been a constant issue since the 1960s, with many of them taking place in the Pacific Region. To understand the Kaiju, you must first understand their origins. Unfortunately for us, no one is entirely sure just where the Kaiju come from. KRSD scientists have some theories, but nothing has been confirmed. No two Kaiju are exactly alike, which makes studying their origins tricky. Listed below are the hypothesized origins of the Kaiju. Although none of these have been officially proven, they are generally considered viable possibilities.

1. NUCLEAR

Probably the most common and potentially dangerous way that Kaiju have been created is through nuclear means. People were not the only ones effected by the 1945 attacks on Japan. Many animals and other wildlife were changed as a result of the radiation, and KRSD researchers believe that the Kaiju are no exception. The most damning evidence supporting this is the fact that almost every Kaiju we have encountered since 1954 has given off varying degrees of radiation. Luckily for us, none of these monsters have been able to harness this nuclear energy. Should that ever happen, and a creature was able to produce nuclear power at will, the results would be catastrophic.

2. SCIENTIFIC EXPERIMENTATION

Mankind has always had a problem with curiosity, and with Kaiju, this is no different. After WWII, many countries attempted to replicate the nuclear weapons exhibited in Japan. When the Kaiju began to appear, however, the nuclear arms race was put on hold. Countries began to fight these emerging creatures and capture them when possible. The captured specimens would then be experimented on in an attempt to learn from them. Some suspect that certain countries were also hoping to replicate these monsters. Most of these specimens were a smaller category of Kaiju, as the bigger ones were very difficult to keep alive, as well as presenting an immense danger to humanity. Some of the countries that were able to capture these specimens include America, Japan, Russia, and Germany. Every so often, a specimen would escape containment and pose a threat to a nearby populace. The risk has been deemed worth the reward, however, as we have been able to gain valuable information on Kaiju and their biology.

3. NATURAL/EVOLUTION

Sometimes, a Kaiju is created not by nuclear energy or mankind's direct efforts, but by nature itself. These Kaiju are natural beasts that some believe have been in seclusion since the Jurassic age. The only reason we are seeing these monsters now is due to the increase in other Kaiju around the world. Some KRSD researchers believe these "Natural Kaiju" to be nature's answer to the other Kaiju destroying the planet. These Kaiju seem to be docile for the most part, not attacking mankind unless provoked. These Kaiju do not often grow that big, but have been reported as even attaining Category III status.

4. EXRTATERRESTRIAL

This origin has only happened on one occasion, and even then, no one is certain. Due to the extreme destruction this Kaiju caused, though, it must be mentioned as a possibility.

In 2013, a meteor struck the country of Russia, knocking out power in the immediate area. Most information on this is classified, but what documents are available suggest that when the meteor was found by scientists, it appeared as though it had been cracked open, almost like an egg. What followed three days later was a Kaiju the likes of which this world has never seen. This event gave the world its first (and so far, only) Category IV Kaiju. This Kaiju terrorized Russia for eight days before finally being put down. Russian scientists still have not been able to find the correlation between the Kaiju and meteor strike, or at least so they say. The only reason this possibility is mentioned is because of the coincidence of the Kaiju appearing days after a meteor crash, as well Russia's behavior regarding the whole situation.

5. UNKNOWN

This last one has happened more often than all other types of origins combined and although it may seem lazy to include it in this description, it is important to talk about it. Part of what makes Kaiju so terrifying is the fact that there seems to be little rhyme or reason to their methods. As hard as it is to conceive, these giant beasts sometimes just appear out of nowhere. These appearances have given the Kaiju an almost mystical presence, with some cultures going as far to worship them as gods. Others believe the Kaiju have been sent to us by the gods to punish us for our evil ways. Whatever the reason, this doesn't change the fact that experts are still baffled by how fast a Kaiju can appear in a highly-populated area and then just disappear as though they were never there, leaving only wreckage in their wake. This leads us to our next point.

WHAT DO THE KAIJU WANT?

This question has baffled mankind since the first appearance of the modern Kaiju, and the short answer is that we have no idea.

Although a Kaiju's origin can explain why they appear where they do, the reason for why they attack is still a mystery. After the first Kaiju appeared in Japan, the Pacific region has seemingly become a breeding ground for these creatures, with the last 73 out of 93 reported Kaiju incidents taking place there. As a result, many of the world's leading Kaiju experts have originated from that region. One of them being Professor Momoko Kochi, who has devoted the last three decades of her life to finding just what makes Kaiju tick. She believes that in order for us to better understand a Kaiju's motives, we must first understand what a Kaiju is.

For starters, Professor Kochi has developed a class and category report in order to better understand how much of a potential threat each Kaiju represents. The report has been used by the United Nations for the last six years in designating Kaiju and is as follows.

KAIJU CLASSES

First, the Kaiju are broken up into four classes, which explain a Kaiju's basic biology and capabilities. It is a very simple system that can be used by civilians and military alike to describe Kaiju sightings.

1. AERO CLASS

The first of the four classes is probably the most dangerous. This class is used to describe Kaiju with the ability of flight. Imagine how much damage a fighter jet can do. Now take that jet, make it ten times bigger, give it teeth, claws, and a bad temper and imagine it is terrorizing your city. These Kaiju have shown to not only cause the most damage, but also are one of the hardest to kill. These beasts are usually very maneuverable and are able to disappear above or below radar level in an instant. These Kaiju are incredibly durable. There was even one report of an Aero Class Kaiju off the coast of Florida that disappeared into a hurricane when the military began to pursue it. This Kaiju was eventually killed, but only after evading the military for a few more days. The hurricane seemed to have no harmful effects on it whatsoever.

2. AQUATIC CLASS

This class of Kaiju has been the most numerous and the most elusive. These Kaiju are primarily based in the ocean or large bodies of water. Whether due to their biology, being unable to breath on the surface, or the fact that an ocean ecosystem can better support such monsters, this class of Kaiju can cause many issues for humans. Besides the obvious fact that a big scary monster hiding under the sea could attack us at any time, these Kaiju disrupt us on a much different level. Almost 90% of all goods are transported by sea. This means that many products and trade rely on the safe and efficient delivery of these giant freighters getting from point A to point B. This can be very hard to do when these ships are essentially sitting ducks on the water for a bored or hungry Kaiju waiting below. As a result, many countries have taken to increasing the size of their Navy, while many companies have begun purchasing advanced security in order to ensure the safe flow of goods. Neither of these solutions have seemed to stop the Kaiju's curiosity, but it has helped guarantee the goods will arrive safely and on time. The crew, however, is a different story.

3. TERRA CLASS

These Kaiju are primarily based on land. They hunt and feed on whatever city or town is in their way and cause a great deal of damage to our ecosystems. In rare cases, these Kaiju have even taken to moving underground. This subterranean method of travel does more damage to the surface then their above-ground counterpart, as these Kaiju disrupt the foundation that many cities and towns are built upon. To make matters worse, these Kaiju usually leave a giant hole or trench where these great cities once stood. Hunting these Kaiju is not the problem, but killing them has proved difficult. They have proven to be more durable than its counterparts.

4. NOVA CLASS

This class deals with Kaiju who are able to travel in and out of space. These Kaiju are still relatively unknown to us and as Professor Kochi explains, the only reason it is talked about is because we believe we have already encountered one like this in Russia. The Nova Class could potentially cripple us against future warfare with the Kaiju, as well as technologically doom mankind. A Kaiju that can travel to or from outer space possesses a unique threat to Earth's satellite systems. These satellites are depended on for much of the technology we use today, including cellular phones and other forms of communication. Not to mention that this Kaiju could be infected with an alien disease that could affect mankind in unknown ways. The other classes are bad news, but what makes this class so frightening is that, until it gets into Earth's orbit, there isn't much we can do to defend ourselves from it.

5. HYBRIDS

Although there are only four classes of Kaiju, it is important to note that in some cases, Kaiju have been shown to "change." Some Kaiju have demonstrated the ability to combine features from the other classes. A common example of this are the Kaiju that blend between the Aquatic and Terra Classes and have been known to terrorize coastal environments. Although we have thankfully not seen it yet, it is not outside the realm of possibility for a Kaiju to evolve. These amazing beasts have shown us time and time again the incredible displays of their natural power. Professor Kochi theorizes that a Kaiju may one day appear that can adapt its body to fit its environment, like many animals do. In that case, the Kaiju could prove to be a scourge for all of humankind and hopefully will be put down immediately.

KAIJU CATEGORIES

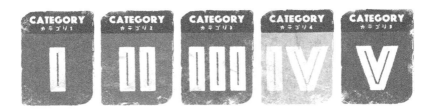

Kaiju have been broken down into five categories to describe their potential threat level. These categories are used to describe the size, weight, and to identify weaknesses within the monsters. It is important to note these categories do not describe every Kaiju's potential abilities, as many Kaiju have at least some sort of energy blast at their disposal. Due to the variance of both effect and severity of these blasts, it is almost impossible to establish a Kaiju's powers along with their categories. These categories are primarily used by civilians when establishing an evacuation plan, or the military when trying to find the most effective way to eliminate the Kaiju menace without escalating the situation.

1. CATEGORY I

These Kaiju are fairly small when compared to the other categories. They usually range from 3-20 feet tall and lack any extra abilities. These monsters traditionally have been referred to as Oni or Ogres in some cultures. Conventional weapons seem to damage them normally. Some possess a few resistances due to their basic biology, but nothing too extreme. These Kaiju can be injured due to fire, cold, electricity, or conventional firearms. Although it is not recommended to face any Kaiju head-on, there have been cases of civilians stopping Category I Kaiju using firearms, booby traps, or in some very rare cases, a blade of some sort, but this is highly discouraged.

2. CATEGORY II

These Kaiju are more common amongst reported attacks and tend to live in more rural areas. They range anywhere from 20-50 feet tall and for the most part, can be affected by fire, cold, electricity, or firearms. It should be noted that unlike the earlier class, there is no record of someone attacking a Category II Kaiju with a blade of any sort and walking away successful. These Kaiju should not be outright approached by civilians and it is advised to attack them from a safe distance.

3. CATEGORY III

This category is where the Kaiju get much more dangerous. Luckily, there have not been too many Category III Kaiju on record. These Kaiju are over 50 feet tall, although they can still be hurt by conventional weapons. Category III Kaiju are usually very durable. Most firearms are not able to penetrate their thick hide. On the off chance that one is able to wound or find an open wound on these Kaiju, it should be exploited. Open wounds will allow elemental-based attacks such as fire, cold, and electricity to do the trick. The problem is wounding the creature to begin with. This usually requires military-grade weaponry to do so. A civilian should never attempt to face a Category III, with or without a group. These monsters will annihilate anything they deem a threat. It is best to evade and wait for the military to deal with them.

4. CATEGORY IV

Category IV Kaiju are the most dangerous Kaiju we have on record. These Kaiju possess the same attributes as the earlier categories, but there are certain traits that automatically qualify them as Category IV, regardless of size or vulnerability. If a Kaiju possesses even one of these abilities, they are instantly a Category IV and are a top priority.

Healing: If a Kaiju is able to heal itself, it is of massive concern. This makes it particularly hard to kill and can force the military to use excessive weaponry. Kaiju with this ability have demonstrated this ability with only a speck of themselves remaining after an attack.

Self-Duplication: In one of the worst incidents in recorded history, a Kaiju appeared off the island of Manhattan in the summer of 1996. It seemed like a typical Category II, Hybrid Class at first, but as it made its way inland, it became apparent that this Kaiju was getting bigger with every innocent bystander it consumed. As the creature grew into a Category III, the military began hitting it with more severe fire-power. The military dropped a barrage of missiles onto the beast, blowing pieces of it all over the city. They believed they had won, but upon inspecting the blast site, the military was horrified to find that the pieces of the monster were not only still moving, they were growing. Every single tentacle, appendage, and inner organ was growing into another creature that scientists feared would grow as big as the creature before it. Five hours after the creature had been blown away, what was left had grown into the size of a large cat. Its arm, which was the only appendage not destroyed, was even starting to grow its shoulder back. Luckily, the military was able to figure out that the creature was vulnerable to fire in this weakened state. They spent the next 24 hours literally burning the city in an attempt to kill the Kaiju. Scientists know very little about this Kaiju, codenamed Mimic, due to them not being able to keep any samples out of fear of the creature reforming. The rest of the creature was transported to a burn pit and its body parts were disposed of there. To this day, there has been no similar creature with the self-duplication ability, but scientists still fear the day that one does emerge. As a result, Kaiju with this ability are automatically a Category IV and should be handled with extreme caution.

Reactive-Adaptation/Self Evolution: A Kaiju with the ability to self-evolve means that it can adapt to its surroundings and change itself accordingly. These Kaiju are always in the Hybrid Class as they are typically able to change their basic anatomy when it comes to fight or flight. The Kaiju could use this ability to strengthen themselves against our weapons. Regardless of what they use it for, this ability is very dangerous as it can lead to the above abilities, which no one wants. Of course, the greatest fear we face with this ability is that a Kaiju evolves so much that we are no longer able to stop it.

5. CATEGORY V

To this day, there has been no Kaiju that has qualified for this category. This category was created as a worst-case scenario that would change the face of our planet as we know it. The categories listed above describe threats that mankind has fought and won against, thanks to our military might. If a Category V Kaiju were to appear, it would pose such an immediate threat to mankind that extreme force would be needed for there to be any hope of mankind being victorious. Category V members would possess one, or potentially both, of the abilities listed below, as well as whatever abilities or traits have been listed thus far in this guide.

Nuclear Ability: Nuclear weapons are the most dangerous weapons in the world. There are somewhere around 15,600 nukes in the world, and 92% of them belong to the United States and Russia. Of those 15,600, only two have ever been used in actual combat, when the United States dropped two bombs on Hiroshima and Nagasaki. As stated earlier, these bombs are what scientists believe gave birth to (or possibly awakened) the modern breed of Kaiju. Although most Kaiju are radioactive in some way, we have never seen one with the ability to weaponize its nuclear energy. If one ever did, not only could its powerful energy destroy anything in its path, but depending on how the beast is destroyed, it may set off a modern-day Hiroshima in its demise. What is even worse is that scientists are not entirely sure nuclear weapons would harm such a creature. If a nuclear Kaiju ever appears, it would care little for eating humans and instead be much more focused on consuming more nuclear energy. Its priority would be to seek out one of the 449 nuclear power plants in the world or the unknown number of nuclear-powered watercraft in the ocean. One thing is for certain, if such a Kaiju were to ever appear, the amount of destruction and lives lost would be unlike anything we have ever seen before.

These bombs get their name from the nuclear reactions used to detonate them, either using fission (a process in atoms that produces tremendous amounts of energy) or fission and fusion reactors to produce large explosions of energy. Due to the many chemical elements of this explosion, an area of attack can have longstanding radioactive effects that are harmful to any nearby organic life. This can lead to radiation poisoning, other diseases, and mutations that destroy life in the most horrible way. These weapons are devastating, with the smallest nuclear weapon—the MK-54 Davey Crockett—having a blast radius of 20 meters, an air blast radius of up to 120 meters, and a radiation radius 430 meters. To put that into context, one of the smallest scale nuclear missiles ever produced would be enough the destroy and highly radiate 1/5 of Central Park, which is 1.317 square miles.

Nuclear energy is released one of two ways. The first being through a process called nuclear fission. In this process, the nucleus of an atom is split into two smaller fragments by a neutron. Nuclear fission is what gave birth to the atomic bomb, which uses power released by splitting the atomic nuclei. Hiroshima and Nagasaki were destroyed by the atomic bomb. The second process is called Nuclear fusion. In this process, two smaller atoms are brought together (usually hydrogen or hydrogen isotopes) to form a larger one. This is the same process the sun uses to produce energy. This is what gave birth to the hydrogen bomb, a bomb that is considered more efficiently destructive than the atomic bomb. The process of nuclear fusion requires high temperatures in order to create its energy, which is often referred to as a thermonuclear explosion. If a Kaiju capable of creating nuclear blasts ever appeared, mankind would face extinction.

Electromagnet Pulse (EMP): In 1958, when America conducted a hydrogen bomb test in the Pacific Ocean, they experienced an unexpected side effect. Hundreds of miles away in Hawaii, street lights were being blown out. At the same time in Australia, people experienced disrupted radio equipment. They didn't realize it at the time, but the United States had just inadvertently created an E-Bomb.

An EMP is an electromagnetic disturbance caused by natural or man-made effects that, depending on the source, cause radiated, electrical, or magnetic disturbances. These disturbances typically originate from a source and disperse in a pulse or waveform from that source. We typically deal with some form of EMPs every day when we hear static on the radio or our television. A much more severe example is lightning, which has the potential to damage both electronics and objects such as buildings or vehicles. When the hydrogen bomb went off, photons from the blast's intense gamma radiation knocked a large number of electrons free from oxygen and nitrogen atoms in the atmosphere. The flood of electrons interacted with Earth's magnetic field to create fluctuating electric current. This electric current created a powerful magnetic field. This is the reason for the intense electrical occurrences across the globe. Since then, the military has attempted to replicate or create a controlled EMP bomb that could disarm military troops in a non-lethal way. Whether the world's military has such a weapon in its arsenal is unknown, however, it would not affect the Kaiju unless they were somehow powered by electrical/magnetic energies. A small magnetic field is harmless in most cases, but a large one with an intense signal would induce a much larger electrical current that could fry the semiconductor components of a radio, melt wiring, or even explode transformers. These intense fluctuating magnetic fields could induce a massive current in just about any other electrically-conductive objects such as phone lines, power lines, or even metal pipes. EMPs vary in intensity with low-level blasts doing nothing more than jamming some electronics. A mid-level blast would corrupt important computer data. A large-scale blast, however, has the capability to completely fry any electronic equipment.

A Kaiju that has EMP capabilities would be incredibly dangerous to all of mankind. This creature could singlehandedly disrupt vehicle control systems, batteries, targeting systems, communication systems, navigation systems, and long/short range sensors. The majority of our military weaponry would be virtually unusable, with the exception weapons that don't rely on computer systems. While an EMP may not destroy missile systems, it would destroy the targeting system and potentially cause the missiles to self-destruct. In the event this creature makes it into a populated area such as a major city, it would make evacuation extremely difficult. The majority of new vehicles (land and air) use an electronic system to operate. Should a Kaiju use its EMP abilities next to a highway, for example, it could bring traffic to a halt. Specialists state that only 40%-60% of automobiles need be damaged in order to cause a complete stop in traffic. A Category V Kaiju could attack a city and completely eliminate any form of escape, making the civilians helpless as the Kaiju feeds upon the population. Should an Aero Class Kaiju have EMP capabilities, it is possible it would be able to knock aircraft out of the sky.

KAIJU ATTRIBUTES

I. Kaiju Biology

Kaiju biology is a tricky thing to define as every Kaiju is physically different from the others. Each Kaiju presents scientists with a myriad of new discoveries and questions. The following is a general description of basic Kaiju biology. It will discuss their physical attributes and anatomy. It should be noted that due to the unique nature of each Kaiju, it is important to remember that these physical attributes could be different if you should ever encounter a Kaiju in the field. Learn what you are able to, but remember, if ever in contact with a Kaiju, be aware of its actions as much as possible. The smallest detail could be the difference between life and death.

A. Durability

All Kaiju, regardless of class or category, are very durable. While all Category I and most Category II Kaiju can be damaged by firearms, it takes a very powerful amount of firepower to finish the job. Once you get into Category III and upward, the firepower required to kill a Kaiju needs to be military-grade and usually requires multiple attacks from different fronts to finish the beast. Although Kaiju can be harmed in conventional ways, they are still very tough, and any attack against them should be done as a last resort if running is not an option.

B. Sight

For the most part, Kaiju see very well, with some even having perfect vision. These Kaiju usually fall into the Aero Class, as they can see from miles away. Some Terra Kaiju have exhibited perfect vision as well, but not to the degree of their Aero brethren. The Kaiju with the worst vision by far are the Aquatic, who seem to depend more on their sense of smell and taste then their actual sight. Kaiju have exhibited the ability to see their prey using a form of thermal vision, but this varies between each monster.

C. Hearing

Kaiju generally hear very well, with most of them relying on their hearing and sense of smell over sight. There have been reports of Kaiju hearing noises from miles away. There have been some Kaiju that appear to actually use a type of sonar (similar to a whale or bat) as their main sense. These Kaiju in particular are very sensitive to noise. In most of those cases, the Kaiju (usually a subterranean monster) attacks due to a painful noise hurting its sensitive ears.

D. Smell

For whatever reason, Kaiju seem to have a very specific sense of smell. This is the one trait that is considered universal amongst all Kaiju. Kaiju have proven to be very susceptible to particular scents, with the smell of meat being the most enticing. KRSD scientists often cite "The Kaiju Attack of Columbus" as a horrible example of this. In 1998, a Category III Kaiju emerged from the earth, codenamed "Buck." When Buck emerged, a large group of people took shelter in the Horseshoe Stadium. As Buck made his way into Columbus, he attacked the city itself, destroying buildings as he made his way down the city streets. Then as eyewitnesses describe it, he seemed to catch the scent of something else. He became almost entranced by this smell, to where he wasn't even paying attention to what little attack he was facing by the National Guard. Buck suddenly took off, sprinting towards the stadium and the helpless people inside. When the National Guard finally caught up to Buck, it was too late. Buck had destroyed the stadium as he crashed into its walls, killing many in the process. They were the lucky ones. The other survivors were trapped in the rubble, with no choice but to watch as Buck began eating them by the handful. Buck was destroyed not too long after this incident, but the damage had been done.

E. Taste

A Kaiju's taste buds are not much different from any other carnivore's. Kaiju seem to prefer fresh meat as opposed to old or decaying meat and there have even been incidents where Kaiju will reject eating a person, because they can smell or taste a sickness within them. Not all Kaiju go out of their way to kill humans specifically, in fact, many Kaiju seem to prefer fish to humans. Many times, a Kaiju will eat chunks of building, concrete, even a full fishing boat, if they have some form of meat inside of them. The Kaiju know what they like, and when they like something, they love it! Doing whatever is necessary to get it.

F. Touch

Not much is known about Kaiju and their sense of touch. They feel pain like any other being, but their impressive size and durability is what protects them from otherwise painful attacks. This is often why a Kaiju can be set upon by a barrage of bullets and seem little more than annoyed. To the Kaiju, it is like being stung by a bee. There have been cases where species of Kaiju rely heavily on their sense of touch to navigate through the area. These Kaiju are believed to be sensing the vibrations in the area and using a type of sonar to map it. Kaiju with this trait have not appeared often, but when using this trait, combined with their sonar, there is no place within a mile radius that is safe from the Kaiju.

G. Decomposition

A Kaiju's death is very messy. When a creature dies, its body usually falls motionless, empties itself of any fluids or waste, and that's about it. When a Kaiju dies, it is a health concern. These creatures empty whatever alien fluids are in their bodies. Their bile, blood, and even waste then spread throughout the area, sometimes damaging structures in the process. The KRSD is usually one of the first on-scene to collect the Kaiju's waste, but sometimes, we are beaten to the punch. Some people and small organizations believe the Kaiju to be gods and that eating a piece of them will grant a person superhuman powers. Please don't be one of these people. Kaiju are radioactive creatures. Although we do not fully understand them, we do understand that eating a piece of them is no different than eating toxic waste. The only thing super that a person can hope to get from eating a Kaiju is super cancer. Luckily for everyone else nearby, there have not usually been any long-term radiation effects to any area near a Kaiju death.

Kaiju will also sometimes implode, releasing their bile, fluids, and body chunks all over the surrounding area. The blast can be fatal to those close to the Kaiju without protection. It is believed this form of death is triggered by the Kaiju as a last-ditch effort to harm its enemies, but the lack of body parts leftover make studying this very difficult.

H. Reproduction

The KRSD has been able to capture only a handful of Kaiju to examine. Of those specimens, none of them are bigger than a Category II. The diversity of these Kaiju has made studying them very difficult. Scientists can only make a few assumptions when it comes to their reproduction. Although the Kaiju in captivity do have reproductive organs, we have never seen them breed. The only time two similar Kaiju of different genders were placed in the same enclosure, they immediately attacked each other until one had eaten the other. This act of aggression startled scientists, as the Kaiju's mood changed from passive to violent as soon as the other was introduced to its confinement. While it seems like Kaiju have the ability to reproduce, it seems they lack the desire.

Scientists have considered the possibility of asexual reproduction. Asexual reproduction is when an organism gives birth to another organism without a sexual partner. We see this frequently in plants and fungi, and in a few amphibians. A creature with this ability gives birth to genetic copies of itself, creating a creature with the same strengths and weaknesses. So far, none of the Kaiju in captivity have demonstrated this trait, but it is still a possibility.

I. Strength and Speed

This may be stating the obvious, but Kaiju are very strong. The heaviest recorded object a Kaiju has been able to lift was a luxury cruise ship estimated at over 60,000 tons.

As far as speed goes, that all depends on the size and anatomy of the Kaiju. Obviously, bigger Kaiju will be able to cover more ground than smaller. Aero Class Kaiju are the fastest, due to the amount of ground they can cover while in the air. Although there has not been any accurate finding for these Kaiju, scientists estimate that, depending on the monster's size and category, Aero Class Kaiju can fly anywhere between 60-300 mph. Aquatic Kaiju are even trickier, as not all Aquatic Kaiju are built for movement underwater. One that is, however, has the potential to swim over 40 mph. These numbers depend heavily on the class and category of the Kaiju, as well as its basic anatomy. As stated above, no two Kaiju are exactly the same. Some Terra Kaiju have legs while the others slither like a snake. It all depends on that particular creature and the environment.

J. Agility

A Kaiju can move very fast when it wants to, however, they usually seem to lumber along as they make their way to their next target. A Kaiju's agility and reflexes are apparent when it comes under heavy fire from the military or other dangers, such as falling buildings or aircraft in the sky. Scientists believe these random spurts of energy are either due to Kaiju not recognizing a threat or need to move fast. When you are bigger than everything else, and cover the distance of 100 feet with each step, it is easy to see how your sense of urgency would be low. Another theory that is gaining popularity with the KRSD eggheads—they hate it when I call them that—is that the

Kaiju are conserving their energy in between attacks, which is why they move so slow.

K. Digestion

Digestion plays a big role in what scientists believe motivates the Kaiju to attack. Put simply, Kaiju attacks on mankind are believed to be motivated by the need to feed. Every living organism needs to consume a certain amount of energy to survive, and Kaiju are no different in this. The average male human needs to consume 2500 calories a day to keep their weight and energy levels consistent, so how much does a Kaiju need to eat every day to function? In order to find a good estimate of this, we need to look no further than Klieber's Law.

Max Klieber was a biologist who observed, for the vast majority of animals, an animal's metabolic rate scales to the 3/4 power of the animal's mass, as shown in the equation below.

$$E = M^{3/4}$$

In the equation, E represents the lowest number of calories an animal needs to eat each day in order to function. The creature's mass (in kilograms) is represented by the letter M, mass is found by multiplying volume by density. So for example, the average Category I Kaiju has a similar mass to that of an African elephant, which is 7000 kg, so would need to eat roughly 53,000 calories a day. How about the largest Kaiju we have encountered to date? That Kaiju, codenamed Indrik, appeared in 2013 during the Russian meteor fiasco. This Kaiju was eliminated by the most powerful non-nuclear weapon in the Russian military's arsenal, the Aviation Thermobaric Bomb of Increased Power (ATBIP), also known as the Father of All Bombs (FOAB). Scientists estimate that Indrik had a mass of 160,000,000 kg, meaning it had to consume at least 99,500,000 calories a day to survive. The average human would yield 110,000 calories if eaten, meaning that he would have had to eat 904 humans a day as a minimum, just to maintain his energy levels.

The need to eat seems to be what motivates most Kaiju attacks, with many Kaiju, regardless of origin, going for the most populated areas. The majority of Kaiju that attack humans are Terra or Aero Class, while the Aquatic Class seems to leave humans alone for the most part. They will occasionally attack a ship or submarine, but scientists believe this is more out of curiosity than out of hunger or aggression. Most Aquatic Kaiju will bite into a vessel to see how it tastes, much like sharks do with humans. The ocean is a big area, full of whales, sharks, and other Kaiju that can sustain most of these monsters' appetites. Kaiju not only require a lot of energy to move around, but also to simply exist. Most Kaiju are powered by some form of nuclear energy and while none (so far) have been able to harness that energy as a nuclear weapon, a few have been able to harness this energy in other ways, such as breathing fire, harnessing electricity, or even shooting lasers out of their eyes. Whatever the case may be, Kaiju need to consume energy to use energy, and when they run low, they will attack the nearest population.

While eating humans is a good way for a Kaiju to regain its spent energy, it is nothing compared to going for the source of Kaiju energy, which is nuclear energy. There are 449 Nuclear Power plants in the world, all of which are stationary and defenseless against the Kaiju threat, despite military guard. When Kaiju have come ashore in the past and began attacking cities or towns, they always seem to sense when a nuclear reactor is nearby. They will immediately head for the reactor. So far, we have been able to stop the Kaiju before they reach any of the nuclear plants. Should a Kaiju ever reach that power source, scientists believe the results would be catastrophic. Not only would the Kaiju cause a nuclear fallout for the surrounding area and contamination of its whole population, but scientists also believe the Kaiju would regain its depleted energy and then some. Scientists fear that this nuclear energy would act as "Kaiju Miracle Grow," jump-starting the Kaiju's chemical biology and morphing it into something more dangerous than before. It is this concern that makes the leaders of the world hesitant to use nuclear weapons on the Kaiju, as well as limiting the amount of nuclear submarines in the sea.

L. Brain Power

A common misconception, at least early in Kaiju research, was that they possessed two brains. This idea was popularized in the 19th century by paleontologist Othniel Charles Marsh, who excavated the remains of a stegosaurus that appeared to have an empty cavity near its rear end. Marsh theorized that the empty space in the large creature could have housed a second brain. For such a large creature to be able to move, some experts theorized it used two brains, one for thinking and the other for movement. Of course this is not the case, as no creature (except one born with two heads) has been shown to possess two brains. With that logic, a blue whale would need two brains to function. However, like most wild ideas, this one ended up in Hollywood, who used it in their science fiction movies and thus popularized it. Kaiju have only one brain. It can be a very large brain, but there is only one.

M. Lifespan

The lifespan of a Kaiju can be difficult to explain. While KRSD has a few Kaiju in captivity that are used for study, they do not provide an accurate depiction of the whole Kaiju race. KRSD currently has five Kaiju in captivity, with the largest one being only Category II. The KRSD Kaiju are kept in a controlled environment and are fed daily.

As long as these monsters behave, they are kept alive. The oldest Kaiju we have was captured in 1998 and as of 2018, is still alive. The creatures in captivity have never been sick. Besides growing in size, they have never even shown signs of aging. Studying a Kaiju in the wild is difficult due their violent nature and no natural habitat. As far as researchers can tell, unless a Kaiju is killed by mankind or unable to feed itself, these creatures just keep on going.

2. Kaiju Behavior

On the surface, these creatures are animals. They want to exist, hunt, and eat like anything else, but the more scientists study them, the more they begin to question the Kaiju's simplicity.

A. Intelligence

As stated before, Kaiju seem to have the basic intelligence of an animal, like that of a wolf, a lion, or any type of predator. Kaiju possess the simplicity to attack a food source when needed to replenish their energy. If they face too big of a threat, most will try to retreat, but some stand their ground and fight until the end. In captivity, the Kaiju have shown basic intelligence. While they do not understand commands like a dog, they seem to understand body posture and facial expressions. Professor Kochi has demonstrated this first-hand. She will approach Kaiju in their environment with a submissive body posture, being careful not to make eye contact. The Kaiju will usually inspect her for a short time and then move on to other things, except with a Kaiju who has not eaten yet that day. The Kaiju in captivity have shown basic problem-solving skills when they can get something out of it, such as food. This does not mean the Kaiju are intelligent beings of unknown origin, however, they are just like most animals wanting to survive.

B. Emotions

Kaiju seem to have emotions like any other creature. They can feel joy or fear, depending on the situation, and respond accordingly. When faced with fear, a Kaiju may lash out in anger or flee. If a Kaiju is excited or happy, then they become very energetic, like a dog, only this dog can knock down a building.

C. Memories

The extent of the Kaiju's ability to retain knowledge is not fully known at this point. We know they retain things such as the location of a food source or possible threats, but that's about it. We are still not sure if a Kaiju has any sense of memory in terms of puzzles or even the beings it interacts with. Professor Kochi jokes that after all these years, they hope the Kaiju wouldn't eat their laboratory personnel should they ever escape, but it is very doubtful.

D. Communication

Kaiju do appear to have some form of communication amongst themselves. Both in controlled environments and in the field, when two Kaiju have come into contact with each other, they have been seen communicating in a series of growls and shrieks, all the while keeping an impressive physical posture. This odd communication ritual almost always ends in the two creatures fighting to the death, with the winner consuming the loser, but there have been cases of one Kaiju retreating. Either way, their communication methods tend to be very primitive and despite what some have said, there is no evidence of Kaiju being able to read thoughts or emotion, aside from what they see in posture or expressions.

E. Motivations

As stated previously, Kaiju seem to have one motivation in life: to survive, and to eat in order to do so. There have not been any known cases of Kaiju reproducing in captivity or the wild, but due to the size of the ocean, it is not an impossible danger. Until it is proven, however, scientists will not acknowledge such a behavior as a motivation.

The second the Americans brought that giant ape to the known world, one thing became very apparent, and that was that we were no longer the top of the food chain. This fact has been made ever clearer to us throughout the years as more and more Kaiju appear, seemingly bigger than the ones previous. Kaiju simply seem to be like any other creature trying to exist in this world, the only difference being this world still belongs to us, something the Kaiju do not seem to grasp nor care about.

F. Social Structure

Kaiju social structure seems to be motivated by one simple rule, and that is that only the strong survive. There have not been any Kaiju on record that worked together like a pack, but if there ever was, that would spell doom for anything in their way. Kaiju will fight each other to the death just for coming in sight of each other. Whether this is done to protect the Kaiju's food source or establish dominance, no one knows.

Dr. Alex Miller from the KRSD has a theory that explains why the creatures would rather fight each other than mankind. He believes that each Kaiju, regardless of origin or category, is in tune with each other. He believes that the Kaiju's pecking order is much more advanced then we give them credit for, with them even having a de facto leader or "king of the monsters," as he puts it. This king, he theorizes, would be the only Kaiju capable of organizing the other monsters. Dr. Miller doesn't think such a king has emerged as of yet, but worries that it is a possibility if the Kaiju continue to evolve.

G. Domestication?

No. Just, no.

While the idea of human beings using Kaiju to fight Kaiju is an enticing one, it is very improbable. If the domestication of Kaiju were to start anywhere, it would be with the captured Kaiju we have had since the early 1960s. During that time, none of the Kaiju in captivity have looked at humans as anything more than suppliers of food. In some cases, the captured Kaiju still view the humans as food, even if they have already been fed. In order for mankind to domesticate another animal, there must be a sense of mutual dependence between to two. For example, we gave wolves food and shelter and in return, they helped us capture more food and protected us. Both parties gained something out of this arrangement. With Kaiju, however, we do not have anything to give them. As far as we can tell, the only thing they want is to eat, which they do not need us for—unless it is to eat us. As a result, the Kaiju do not depend on mankind enough for us to domestic them. Maybe we will figure out other motivations amongst the Kaiju one day and domestic them with that, but until that day comes, they are just our competition for the top of the food chain.

MONKEY
BUSINESS

Glenn Rock, New Jersey

It is unseasonably warm this time of year in New Jersey. The sunlight is breathing life into the small pond near the Glen Rock Veterans' Home. Major Micheal "Rolex" Rockwell walks along the stream, throwing pieces of bread into the duck-filled pond as we go. The 87-year-old veteran hobbles along, but with a determination not usually seen for someone his age. Despite his age, Micheal does not seem to be slowing down physically or mentally as he recounts his time in the military.

I entered pilot training on my 22nd birthday. It was a time for rebuilding, not just for Americans but the rest the world too. World War I had ended 12 years prior and everyone was focused on getting back to life before the war. This means a lot of people were getting out of the military. For me, though, the military was never about

43

fighting wars or defending the country. For me, it was a way to chase my passion for flying. I grew up on a farm in southern New York, where my father was one of the first farmers to embrace crop-dusting. He would take my brother and I up in the plane with him and teach us the ins and outs of flying. I fell in love with the sky, and for me, flying just always made sense. I think that is what ultimately drove me to the military.

We settle onto the picnic table near the pond. Major Rockwell throws the rest of his bread into the pond, much to the ducks' delight.

I suppose you want me to talk about the fucking gorilla, don't you?

This bold question catches me off guard, a fact I'm sure is painfully obvious by my surprised expression.

Calm down, son, I'm just having a little fun with you. Of course we are going to talk about the gorilla. That thing has come up in every barroom conversation, holiday party, and anniversary report since 1933. I don't mind telling the story, I just wish people wanted to talk to me more about aviation rather than monsters from the past.

That story starts in 1933. I was stationed at Mitchel Field. It wasn't a bad location for a base, we were on Long Island, which meant there was always something to do. I had graduated pilot training three years prior, at the top of my class, and my attitude reflected that. I was a cocky son of a bitch. I didn't have a drinking problem or a get into fights like some soldiers. I truly did feel that I was the best pilot the Air Corps had to offer. I would get easily bored with the military side of things, though. I just wanted to fly, just wanted to get my plane and go out into the world.

This attitude got me into more trouble than it got me out of. I was constantly late for roll call and training drills because I quite frankly didn't see much of a point. As far as I was concerned, I didn't need the training. Unlike most of these guys, I had been flying since I was a teenager. This problem with punctuality eventually earned me the callsign "Rolex." A callsign that my squadron commander hoped would shame me into taking the military side of things more serious and after a lengthy "discussion," I began to see things his way. However, every once in a while, I would like to remind them why they gave me the callsign in the first place. [**smiles**]

How soon were you aware of what was happening in New York City?

Not soon enough. [**Major Rockwell reaches into his jacket pocket and pulls out a pack of cigarettes and begins to smoke**]. Information traveled so differently back then, we were only an hour, maybe an hour and a half, away from everything, but by the time we found out about what had happened, the gorilla had already escaped and wreaked havoc all over the city. I don't know if the police were trying to keep the situation contained on their own or if it simply just didn't occur to them to get some sort of air support, but it took a while. I don't blame the police for their slow reaction, I just think that had we been alerted sooner, we could have put the beast down a lot sooner. We didn't end up finding out about what had happened until almost three hours after it had escaped and even then, we weren't given much info.

What information were you given?

We were told that a large gorilla had escaped from a Broadway show and was terrorizing downtown New York. We knew that it had killed a few civilians and that police had the area surrounded.

Did you have any idea just how large the creature was?

Some...

We had heard the radio broadcasts and seen the newspaper clippings about this giant ape from a mysterious land, but we didn't put much stock into that. It was the 1930s, there were all sorts of shows at the time that claimed to have some sort of monster. It always turned out to be nothing more than a hoax. I don't think any of us assumed that the gorilla running around the city was the same monster that had been advertised in the newspapers.

So, what was the plan?

Simple. We were supposed to find the damn monkey and signal the police once we did.

So, not kill it?

Negative! Our guns were too inaccurate, and the area was still full of civilians. We were to find the monster and signal to the police using our flares. If we were lucky enough to find the gorilla out in the open and away from civilians then we were allowed to fire on it, but our primary objective was to help the police track the damn thing.

What happened?

By the time the call came into the base, we had all mostly gone to bed. We got woken up at around 0400 in the morning by our flight chief. By 0430, we were getting briefed on the situation, most of us still groggy or hungover from the night before. Looking back, I don't think that we grasped just how serious the situation was. The whole thing sounded pretty ridiculous. Our flight finally took off at around 0500 from Mitchel Field. Our squadron had just received the brand-new Curtiss O2C model airplane. This airplane would eventually be known as the Helldiver and was very prominent in the early years of World War II. At the time, it was still considered experimental. Our flight commander thought this was a good chance to test the Curtiss in the field. By today's standards, the plane is considered a dinosaur, but back in the 1933, these things were state-of-the-art. They had two fixed machine guns mounted on the front and were capable of flying over 130 mph. We felt damn near invincible in one of these things. I remember thinking that I wished my dad could see them in action. It sure would have blown his mind to see just how far we had come in such a short amount of time.

How many of you were there?

We took off as a flight of four. Each aircraft had a pilot in the front seat and a rear seat gunner. The planes didn't have any guns attached to the back of them, so the gunners would have to fire a handheld machine gun from the back. It takes a steady hand to do that and a great deal of trust between the pilot and the gunner, so no one got shot in the back. [smiles] Luckily, my rear gunner just happened to be my buddy, Captain Stanley "Golden" Goldberg. We had met in pilot training. Our superiors paired us up as a way to even each other out. I was a brash, hotshot pilot and Goldie was a calm, quiet guy. I think they were hoping our personalities would rub off on one another, but I don't think that ever happened. I was always an asshole, and Goldie, bless his heart, was always trying to keep me in line. After the war ended, I ended up marrying Goldie's sister. Luckily, he didn't know I was dating her at the time, otherwise he may have shot me in the back. [laughs] I never knew if they gave Goldie his call sign because of his last name or because it was some attempt to make fun of him for being a Jew. Regardless, Goldie accepted his callsign with no complaints. Our flight chief would often call us by our callsigns when talking to us. It wasn't long before we were known as "Gold'n Rolex." Of course, he usually didn't call us this unless we, mostly me, was in some sort of trouble. Poor Goldie wound up being my babysitter for most of our time in the service. Looking back at it, I'm actually very amazed that he never shot me in the back.

How soon before you found the creature?

Not long. It took about 20 minutes for us to get in to the city. The fog was thick. Of course, it wasn't long before we realized that it wasn't fog at all. It was smoke from all the fires downtown. When the report came in, it only detailed that a large gorilla had escaped its confinement and was terrorizing Broadway. The report made no mention of the gorilla's size being over 40 feet or the extent of damage this thing had done. When we emerged from the smoke, we saw cars that had been crushed and flipped. We even saw some that appeared to have been thrown. I have a particular image in my head of a police car that had been thrown and impaled on a street light...

I couldn't tell if the officers were still inside. It was very dark. If things were not illuminated by fire or still functioning street lights, then we didn't see all that much. It was what we could hear, those sounds are what still stick out to me. Even with the sirens going on, you could still hear people screaming, so much screaming. I heard a woman looking for her son, repeatedly yelling his name, yelling for her little boy Samuel. [**Micheal's face changes from its calm demeanor to very focused and pained look**] I could hear random gunshots going off, but I'm not sure if they were coming from the police, civilians, or even what they were shooting at. As we got closer to the ground, the noise eerily disappeared entirely. That was when we saw him standing in the middle of the street, and that was when I knew that we were in for a fight.

Did he know that?

The hairy son of a bitch threw a fucking street light at us as soon as he saw us, so yeah, I would say that he knew why we were there.

Did you start shooting then?

Negative. I think when we first saw him, we were in somewhat disbelief. When he first saw us, I think he just saw another predator that was challenging his domain. He threw the light like a spear right into the middle of our formation. It was a miracle that we were able to avoid it in such tight quarters. We flew past him and were setting up to come back around, but when we did, the damn thing had disappeared.

How could something so big disappear so easily?

I've been asked that a lot over the years. If this thing was so large and terrifying like we said it was, then how come it was able to avoid us and the police for so long? The only thing I can come up with is that this monster that we have built up in our heads was little more than a terrified animal. Knowing what I know now, about how they found this creature on some strange island, the method with which they captured it, and the fact that it wasn't coherent until it finally woke up on display in front of hundreds of people, it's no wonder why he reacted the way it did. If all you know your entire life was brutality, brutality that made you king of your domain, and then you're suddenly taken to some strange new place, I'd wake up pretty pissed off too.

So, do you feel sympathy for this creature?

Fuck no. The thing was a menace and it needed to be put down. I'm just saying that it acted according to its nature.

You eventually found him again?

Within a matter of minutes. All we had to do was follow the noise and flying debris. It was very clear just from a first glance that no police gun would be able to take this thing out. We were now shooting to kill. Our guns were ready to fire, but that didn't end up happening.

Because of the girl?

Yes, because of the girl. Somewhere between throwing a street light at us and making his way to the Empire State Building, this guy decided to pick up a hitchhiker. Some poor actress type, from what I understand. This poor girl wasn't even at this creature's unveiling, she was right across the street seeing some other show, but of course it didn't matter to the gorilla. I'm not sure why he grabbed her. If she stuck out to him for some reason or if she was just some random person in the crowd that he managed to grab. Regardless of the reason, by the time we got turned around and found him, he was carrying her in one hand and climbing up the Empire State Building with the rest of his appendages. People always ask us why we didn't fire on him then and there, to stop him before he took her up there. The reality is that even though our plane was state-of-the-art back then, maneuvering it was still tricky, and flying in between the skyscrapers of New York made it even trickier. On top of that, we did not want to risk firing at him and hitting her. Even if we did hit him, then odds are he would have fallen to his death with her still in hand. I think we were collectively trying to figure out a way to deal with him and keep her alive. So while we circled the building, he continued to climb. Eventually, our flight lead, Major Bisbing, signaled for us to get back into formation. Once we reformed, he told us to "buzz him."

Buzz him?

Fly past it, get close to him and scare the shit out of him. I think the hope was that he would get scared and decide to climb down, but that never ended up happening. The damn thing was able to get to the top as we were getting in formation. We broke off and flew two by two, coming at him from both sides, and for a little while, it looked like it would work. He was getting so startled by us, it seemed like he was becoming unbalanced. He even put the girl down on the ledge so that he could steady himself. We were sure that he would be on his way down any minute. Boy, were we wrong. On the third flyby, the gorilla became very unsteady and had to grip the building just to stay on top. Once he settled himself back, his body language seemed to change. It was noticeable in his face first. Where he had looked terrified just a few seconds ago, now he looked determined and pissed off, quite frankly.

What happened next?

Major Bisbing was never one to rush into any situation. Usually to my disdain, he would watch a situation unfold from a distance, waiting to strike at the most opportune moments. It was for that reason that he was considered by many of our peers to be the best pilot in our squadron. That is why what happened next, I think, was so emotional for us. Major Bisbing saw the creature steady himself and thought that this was the moment to end it. He made a sharp turn around and went straight for that damn gorilla, guns blazing. If he had just stayed in formation, then you would be interviewing him right now instead of me, but as soon as he made that sharp turn, him and Lt. Alverez, his rear gunner, were met by the actress in midair. He had thrown that girl like a ragdoll, right in to the front cockpit. What we saw next was a splatter of blood and guts followed by an explosion as the plane proceeded to take a nosedive. The thing that sticks out to me the most was the look on that poor girl's face. The whole thing couldn't have lasted more than a few seconds, but as soon as we turned around to see what was happening, the girl was in midair coming straight at the plane. The worst part was that she was conscious the entire time. She was fully aware of the fact that she had just been thrown to her doom. The look of terror on her face, followed by the screams of panic and pain as the pilots burned alive while the plane plummeted to the city streets below, is something I will never forget.

Major Rockwell takes a long puff of his cigarette, his hands trembling the entire time.

After that, everything was kind of a blur. I remember seeing Major Bisbing's plane go down, remember the screams, and the smell of burning jet fuel, but then I think I went into shock. Not out of fear, you understand, but out of anger. These were men who, despite our differences, were like brothers to me. These men had families back home, with Lieutenant Alverez just celebrating the birth of his little boy. I was pissed, and in that moment, I was ready to unleash every bit of hell on this giant fucking ape. It wasn't me flying that plane. In that moment, all of my training and my passion for flying went out the window. With tears rolling down my face and me screaming at the top my lungs, all I could think was, Kill! Kill! Kill! Kill!

I was firing at him with everything that I had. I'm not sure if I ran out of ammo or if my guns jammed, but eventually, they stopped firing and I was still flying directly at him. Luckily, I had Goldie in the backseat to snap me out of whatever rage I was in. I heard him say, "pull up, dummy, you got him" as I began to climb and make my turn back around to him again or at the very least distract him so the other two planes could finish the job. As we turned back around, it was pretty clear the gorilla was in a bad way. He was standing on two legs, but his feet looked like they were going to give out from under him at any moment. He looked like he was in a daze and it wasn't until I got closer that I saw the pools of blood starting to form below him. I don't know if it was me or one of the other planes, but he was shot right by the heart and it was clear he didn't have much longer. In one final act of aggression, he steadied himself and with whatever strength left in his body, let out a bloodcurdling roar that I'm sure was heard all over New York City. He began to pound his chest like some war drum as we continued to fly towards him. He took one step forward and then jumped towards us in what I'm guessing was some last attempt to take us down with him. He was a fighter, the fucker, I'll give him that. Luckily for us, we were still far enough away that even with his impressive jump, he still fell a few feet short, and me and Goldie watched as the look of anger on his face disappeared and terror emerged as he fell to the streets below.

And then it was finally over?

More or less. We had a parade afterwards to celebrate the victory over the escaped animal and to honor those that were killed during its rampage. The six of us were in the spotlight for a little bit, with all of us, I think, believing that we contributed to that final kill shot. Who actually finished off the monster though, I'll never know for certain. A few years later, World War II broke out and people seemed to forget about us entirely. With Pearl Harbor and the Nazis, Americans had bigger concerns then remembering some zoo animal attack. Of the six of us that survived the gorilla, only three of us returned home from the war. Unfortunately, Goldie was not one of them. I married his sister Maria shortly after returning home and we made a pretty great life for ourselves, had a few kids, and enjoyed what good times we were able.

Is there anything you regret about the incident on the Empire State Building or anything that followed? Do you think that we can learn anything from what happened in 1933?

Of course. I regret the lives that were lost, especially Major Bisbing and Lieutenant Alverez. As for how things could've been handled differently, I think that we would have reacted in the same way. We weren't trying to hurt anybody and regardless of how some people feel, our main goal was to keep everyone safe. I think that our situation with the gorilla in 1933 was a precursor to what has happened since the war ended. I wish the war never took place for a lot of reasons, but the biggest one is because I believe it weakened us. While we were busy fighting each other, this new enemy was getting stronger and we didn't even realize it because we were too busy bickering like children. I can only hope that in the future, mankind will work together to go against this greater threat, but that petty bickering doesn't seem like it's gonna stop anytime soon.

Major Rockwell passed away peacefully in his sleep a few weeks after giving this interview. His account of the earliest known Kaiju attack has been invaluable to the KRSD and its research team.

AKUMA

Mako Island, Japan

I arrive to the modest Mako Island, where I am interviewing Eiji Yoshida, a fisherman who has lived on the island his whole life. Yoshida-San is one of the only witnesses still alive that saw the very first modern Kaiju attack on Japanese soil. With the help of my translator Paul, I ask him to recount his experience during the beginning days of the Kaiju attack.

I think we knew that something was wrong within the first few days of the creature coming into our waters. Fishing had been bad the days leading up to the attack, during a time of year where it should've been plentiful. It wasn't until we started to get whale carcasses washing up on shore that we started to panic. I remember the village elders thinking that it was some sort of curse. They demanded a ritual be performed in order to cleanse the islands of their misfortune. It wasn't just our island that was experiencing these issues, but all of the islands around us as well. We pleaded with the government for some help, but did not receive any. I think they just assumed it was rotten luck and there was nothing they could do. Fishing was a big deal for us. The islands offered little in sustenance and no fish meant that people would go hungry. Luckily, we had a good community amongst the villages. We helped each other out however we could, sharing food as needed.

When were you made aware of the ships that had vanished off the coast?

At first, we were only told about the one. The first ship vanished within the same week that our problems started. Some people thought that it was destroyed due to a storm, while others thought attacked by a U.S. warship. Our village elders still held onto the fact that the seas were cursed. I didn't buy that. I was 15 at the time and didn't have much patience for superstition. I, like many other people in the village, just assumed it was bad luck. It didn't come out until a few years later that three ships had vanished off the coast, not just one. Apparently, the government had some suspicions, but didn't want to alarm the public. I think they were worried about the possibility of us being on the receiving end of another attack from the U.S.

For two weeks, the only issues we had on our island were the lack of fish. We kept an eye out for any wreckage from the missing vessels, but nothing ever turned up. It wasn't until the end of the second week when the neighboring Tomo Island was attacked. I was out with my father and uncle fishing that day. We had been out all day in hopes of trying to fish something out of the ocean, but had no luck. Our island was right next to Tomo Island, close enough that we could swim to it on a calm day. The wind had started to pick up as the sun began to set. My uncle was saying how he could feel a storm brewing. The poor man had no idea how right he was. We returned home and set up for supper. The wind started to howl outside just as we finished eating. The storm had started, and it was fierce. Rain pelted our roof and thunder shook the skies. I remember I was having an awful dream about the storm clouds eating my loved ones before finally coming after me. Just as the storm swallowed me whole, I was woken up by my father. He didn't wake me because of my nightmare, though. He woke me because we began to hear the bells.

The bells?

In those days, telephones were not as common on the islands. In order to signal that something was wrong, each island had a large bell placed at different points along the inland. These bells were used to notify its residents about an emergency. When we emerged from our home, we saw Tomo Island, and it sounded like a war was taking place over there. It wasn't our island's bells that were going off, it was theirs. We looked over to Tomo island and saw its residents fleeing into the sea. My father and I rushed to our fishing boat so that we could go to shore and help the people however we could. We had no idea what was happening on the island. Whatever was creating the distress seemed to be coming from the other side of the island. At first, we thought it was the storm, but that changed as we got closer to the island. It was so strange how the storm clouds stayed over Tomo, almost like they were attacking the island. We were soon joined by a few other fishermen from our island as we floated towards Tomo. People were still frantically running to the sea, some of them covered in blood. As we got closer, we saw that parts of the island were on fire. I remember, so many people were screaming. I thought the island had been hit by lightning or something. It wasn't until some of the islanders began to come aboard our boat that I thought otherwise. They kept screaming about something being after them and urging us to get away from the island as fast as we could. So many people were trying to get onto our boat. It got to the point where we were so full of people that my father started threatening people with his oar. If we took any more people, then our boat would have sunk. We kept trying to tell them, but they didn't care. They were just trying to get away from the island as fast as possible. That is when we heard a roar come from the island and everyone stopped. The fires disappeared and Tomo Island was covered in complete darkness. Everyone was motionless during that time. I heard the roar for the second time and it sent chills down my spine. I was so, so scared that I actually wet myself. We then heard what sounded like heavy footsteps and then nothing. The storm clouds disappeared and the island was silent. We didn't see the creature of the island, but that roar has been with me since that night.

KRSD HQ, Tokyo, Japan

After hearing Yoshida-san's firsthand account about this horrendous attack, I decided to look further into this Kaiju, which is now known as Akuma. I have taught an interview with Dr. Hiroshi Okada, a legendary member of the KRSD. Dr. Okada is a paleontologist and was part of the original team that went to Tomo Island to investigate the Akuma incident. It was this incident that led Dr. Okada and the other members of the seven-person research group to found the KRSD. Although he does not actively work in the field anymore, Dr. Okada is still active within the KRSD as a liaison of sorts. He has published countless books on Kaiju and is best known to Western audiences for his television special "Dr. Okada's Kaiju World," a six-part miniseries that appeared in the 80s. That series was the first of its kind, offering audiences a transparent look into the mystery and horror of the Kaiju.

Well, of course the incident at Tomo Island created some issues for the government. Not only had they been trying to keep the stories of all the missing ships a secret, but now they had a whole island of people that had disappeared seemingly overnight. Public outcry was intense, and they needed to do something fast. I don't think anyone believed the stories of the giant monster, though. No one had seen anything and quite frankly, any of the proof that the locals brought to us could've been disproven. It is one thing to see a photograph of a giant footprint, but another thing entirely to actually stand within the footprint. The government sent myself and a few others out to investigate Tomo Island. I was a paleontologist. If there was anything prehistoric on this island, it was my job to identify. The rest of the team members came from the other fields of study. We had a biologist, a botanist, zoologist, an ecologist, and a few other researchers who came to inspect the area for any radiation.

What did you find?

What didn't we find? We all believed that a giant storm had done all this damage and that the villagers were just superstitious. Once we got to the island though, it was an entirely different story. The island was covered in footprints from something that was too large to be any natural creature on the island. We were actually standing in one of the footprints. There is a famous photo of it. We put the entire research team and a few of the islanders in the footprint and still had room left over. Whatever made these tracks was easily over 100 feet tall. We also inspected the area for any other signs of the creature. We found some scales and some fragments of what we believed to be teeth, and perhaps most damning of all were the prehistoric trilobites found on the island. A trilobite is a marine arthropod that was believed to be extinct for the last 250 million years. These creatures were believed to have lived on larger creatures, as a type of prehistoric parasite. At that point, I was convinced that we were not dealing with any island superstition or supernatural creature, but instead believed it to be a kind of dinosaur that had somehow survived all these years underwater.

Did you have any theories how this may have happened?

I had many theories. We all did. Between the seven of us, I think each person had at least 10 ideas. Each one of us found something on that island that was a complete gamechanger for our fields of study. None of us knew exactly what we had found or what type of creature we were dealing with. We inspected the remains, or lack thereof, of the villagers that were killed during the attack. What we found was conclusive with everything else in that we were dealing with something that was very large. Perhaps the most alarming of all, though, were the radiation readings that were taken on the island. The radiation had been through the roof, and had we known, we would have dressed appropriately. Luckily, there has been no lasting damage. The radiation decreased as the day went on, being almost nonexistent by the time we left the island.

Once you got your findings in order, what did you do?

Myself and the other team members presented our findings to a council of government officials. It was a closed-door meeting, meaning that the press were not invited. I was fully expecting to be ridiculed and laughed out of the building. Telling people that a giant dinosaur was terrorizing the seas was the quickest way I could've discredited myself. We showed them the photographs of the footprint and villager remains. We read off the radiation findings, and even brought the remains of a trilobite to show the council. After our briefing, there was a long silence in the room. All of the government officials were just looking at us and their notes, visibly perplexed. Finally, the chairman began to speak. The first thing he asked was if we thought such a creature could be killed. This surprised and relieved us all the same time, because it showed that they were taking this matter just as serious as us.

We continued to discuss matters further with the small council and gave input however we were able to. Over the next few days, we were able to set up a contingency plan with the military for what to do if the creature should make land at any of the more populated islands. Specifically, we were worried about Tokyo. My team had access to whatever resources we needed. I think the government realized the danger that such a creature possessed and wasn't willing to take any chances. Our small team of researchers was the earliest iteration of the KRSD, but it was quite a few years before we were given that name. Our mission, given to us by the government, was to investigate any possible Kaiju attacks and work with the military leaders in order to build contingency plans. If a Kaiju made landfall, it was our job to have countermeasures in place. Of course, the creature did eventually come to Tokyo. We were prepared, but that's not to say that everything went smoothly.

Dr. Okada gave me much insight into the early days of not just the KRSD, but the Kaiju as well. These creatures were new to a world that had just been at war for the last few years. They quite literally could not have showed up at a worse time. Even though it was a time of rebuilding, international relationships were shaky at best. The fact that the Kaiju were somehow linked to nuclear activity also lead to much hostility towards the United States. Although it has never been proven, many countries still believe that these creatures are a direct result of nuclear testing. That is why, when Akuma began terrorizing the Japanese people, Japan elected to handle the situation themselves. They wanted to keep the matter private and avoid outside interference. According to Dr. Okada, for a country that had just suffered so much, its leaders wanted to show that they could still stand on their own two feet.

San Fransisco, California

My third and final interview about Akuma is conducted with former Tokyo Police Officer, Hiroshi Serizawa. Officer Serizawa left his home in Tokyo and moved to the United States in the 1960s, where he now resides in San Francisco, California. Officer Serizawa was just beginning his career when he faced the dreaded Kaiju now known as Akuma.

Well, I was a traffic cop back then. It wasn't a glamorous job, but I was just beginning my career in law enforcement and you have to start somewhere. I grew up in Tokyo. My father and brother died in the war. It was just me and my mother left, and it was my job to take care of her. Truth be told, I actually liked being a traffic cop. I got to interact with many people that I grew up with and felt like I was helping my community, even if it was just directing traffic. Of course, I was teased by a few people I grew up with, but I didn't get too discouraged. I just kept working hard and doing as I was told, and I figured things would work out okay in the end.

Did you know about Tomo Island or the ships that went missing?

We were made aware of the ships, but we were only told about one of them. Of course you hear rumors about things, but the government kept everything pretty quiet. I don't think they even let the Tomo Island survivors out in public until they got a handle on the creature. Besides a few rumors though, we had no idea. When the Akuma finally did show up, the government was ready, but the citizens of Tokyo were not.

Could you take me through that day?

Started like any other—I woke up, I ate breakfast with my mother, she hounded me about finding a wife, and then I went to work. It was sunny. The world was normal. After my lunch is when things started to get strange. I stopped for lunch at a café when it came over the radio that a large shipping vessel had appeared to sink near Tokyo Bay. What was even more strange was the fact that shortly after this announcement, soldiers began to walk around the streets of Tokyo. They were just patrolling at first. And then it started to rain. Not heavy rain, just a light drizzle. Regardless though, as soon as it started to rain, the bomb sirens began to sound and the soldiers began evacuating people.

I wasn't told anything by the soldiers, just that I needed to block traffic from the main road and urge everyone to go towards the evacuation points. I called my superior officer, who proceeded to chew me out and told me to "not ask stupid questions and just do as I was told." Within the hour, my whole patrol area had been almost completely evacuated. After that, the soldiers relieved me of my post and told me to join the civilians. I kept asking questions about what was going on, about the bombers, who was attacking, and how far out they were. Instead of an answer, I received nothing more than a few grunts and the repeated order to evacuate. It wasn't until further pressing one of the soldiers that he told me it wasn't a bomb but a storm and that I still needed to evacuate the area.

Instead of evacuating though, I returned home to my family's apartment to check on my mother. I wanted to make sure that she was no longer there. I returned home to an empty apartment and was able to breathe easy, but not for long. The apartment began to shake. It was subtle at first, but each tremor felt more and more powerful than the last. I looked out the apartment window to see what was causing such a ruckus, when suddenly a giant dark figure appeared right in front of my apartment building. The tremor from his steps was enough to knock me off balance. I remember thinking that the building was going to collapse. It was at that moment that I heard the darkness roar. It was so loud that all of the windows in the apartment building shattered, spraying glass everywhere. I shielded myself from the spray of glass and then sat on the floor of my apartment, horrified at what I had just seen. The creature kept walking and I could begin to hear the sound of gunfire in the distance. I sat there for a very long time, too afraid to move.

What snapped you out of it?

I heard a little girl crying outside my apartment window. She was calling for her mother. I must've sat there for over an hour, but as soon as I heard the sound of that girl, something snapped inside of me. I was still wearing my uniform, and I was still a police officer. I stood up, dusted myself off, and made my way out into the city streets to find a lost child. I found her wandering in the street, just a few feet from my building. The girl's name was Kimiko and she had lost her mother during the Akuma's arrival. Poor girl could not have been more than four years old. I held Kimiko in my arms and together we walked the city streets, attempting to find shelter. Over the next few hours, I was able to gather more survivors, finding them hidden throughout the city. These people were trying to hide, but as soon as they saw a police officer, they figured that I was the safest person to be around. I just remember feeling overwhelmed. I had no idea what I was doing. I had no plan. I myself was just a scared child wearing a policeman's uniform, but these people depended on me. I made a pledge to myself that I was going to do whatever needed to be done in order to keep them safe.

Tokyo was like a warzone. We could hear the creature roaring in the distance and the sounds of artillery strikes all around us. I was praying that those strikes would not find us by accident. We were finally able to navigate our way to an underground bunker. One of many that was scattered throughout the city during the war. These bunkers were supposed to defend us from bombings. I hoped it would be enough to withstand the might of the creature and our own military. I made sure everyone was safely underground before I shut the door. I stopped to look at the horizon before I shut it. Tokyo was burning and this creature was standing in the distance, relishing in the destruction it had caused. Its roar was the last thing I heard as I shut the door and climbed below into the bunker.

It was hours before the tremors from artillery strikes faded. It was a few more hours after that before we decided to go aboveground and check on the situation. The sun had started to rise over the horizon, the flames that engulfed Tokyo had disappeared, and the creature that terrorized our city was lying dead over the debris. The military had won. It was a hard-fought battle, but we survived. It was a long road ahead in terms of rebuilding, but we managed.

The political climate was intense, to say the least, after the attack. I remember a lot of finger-pointing was going on. A few months later, the United States dealt with its own Kaiju attack. It soon became clear that the world was changing and that mankind was going to have to change as well, if we hoped to survive. I was promoted for my bravery during the attack and went on to have a fairly successful career as a police officer. Over the years, more Kaiju attacks took place and we were always left standing, broken but standing. I eventually settled down and started my own family. It wasn't too long after that that we decided to move to the United States in attempt to get away from the Kaiju. Of course we still had our issues with them, but it was not as prevalent as it was in Japan.

Serizawa-san spent nearly 40 years as a part of the Tokyo Police Department. He and his family eventually moved to San Francisco after he retired. Serizawa-San says that he moved to the United States in an attempt to get his family away from the Kaiju. It should be noted that in an odd set of coincidences, both his son and daughter are members of KRSD. They are continuing their father's legacy of keeping innocent people safe by trying to rid the world once and for all of the Kaiju menace.

THE MILITARY VS. THE KAIJU

The Military Element

The military is the greatest weapon the human race has in its fight against the Kaiju. A diligent survivalist could acquire an impressive artillery over a period of time, but they will never have access to the same level of training, resources, and effective weaponry that the military. We will cover civilians fighting against the Kaiju in a later section. In this section, we will discuss the military tactics used during a Kaiju attack. This section is designed to give you a better understanding of the theater of battle and allow you to better work with the military in order to survive that attack. If you are aware of basic military practices/strategies, then you will be able to plan your survival more effectively. Make no mistake, the military will try and help you however they can, but their main priority will be to mitigate the overall risk to the rest of the human population. This sometimes means a potential disregard for civilians in the immediate proximity of the Kaiju. If the military needs to stop a rampaging Kaiju from reaching a nuclear reactor a few miles away and the only option available is to bomb it immediately, then that may be the best option overall.

Military Priorities

The military has a very specific set of priorities when responding to a Kaiju attack. Below are the priorities in order of highest down to help you understand basic military protocol.

1. Eliminate the Kaiju

The first priority is to eliminate the threat, which in this case is a Kaiju. This does not mean that the military will bomb the monster into oblivion with no regard to civilian lives. What it does mean is that eliminating a massive threat to the rest of the population is the top priority. Should the military be unable to eliminate the Kaiju menace, its new priority would be to contain and if possible, reroute the Kaiju to an area where it could do less damage. Considering that most of these monsters originate from the sea, rerouting them back to there would seem like the most advantageous method to cause the least number of civilian casualties.

2. Protect Civilians/Key Resources

The military will aid local offices—such as law enforcement, fire department, and other first responders—with the protection and safe evacuation of civilian personnel. The military will attempt to transport civilians out of harm's way so they do not get caught in the crossfire between themselves and the rampaging Kaiju. Key resources that the military would protect include but are not limited to nuclear reactors, airports, hospitals, or any other location that may house important personnel or resources. Buildings with potentially hazardous materials/ diseases should be evacuated immediately. Although these buildings would be protected, the additional harm done to the surrounding area would be catastrophic should a Kaiju destroy one of them.

3. Aid with rebuilding

The military's final priority is helping with the initial rebuilding of destroyed areas. This responsibility would go to the local government, but the military would be present for the beginning stages. Unless the area has any high risk/key resources, the National Guard would handle the majority of this, with the active duty military members returning to their assigned bases.

Military Vs. Kaiju

The KRSD has worked with military forces around the world to ensure they have an immense amount of resources at their disposal when dealing with the Kaiju threat. How they choose to dispatch these behemoths depends largely on the class, category, and location. Before we break down the tactics, let's first look at the tools at our disposal.

TOOLS

1. TROOPS

Our greatest tool in the theater of war is the well-trained men and women of the armed forces around the world. Without these professionals, we would not stand a chance against the Kaiju menace. Our special forces operatives go through rigorous training that, depending on the branch and organization, can take years to complete just to be accepted into the team. Human beings have been the top of the food chain for a long time, and it is because of our military personnel that we are still in contention for this title. The only limits possessed by the military are those placed on them by their superiors or that of the general public.

2. SERVICE RIFLES

Each military branch, regardless of its country of origin, trains each and every one of their members to use a firearm. Although the type of firearm differs by country, the typical weapon is a highly versatile and durable assault/battle rifle of some sort. These rifles are often selected for their versatility and reliability on the battlefield, and the fact that they can be modified to better suit varying situations.

It is also important to note that durability does not always equal reliability. As many service members are quick to point out, their weapons are made by the lowest bidding contractor. A more elite, or battle-trained, soldier is also trained in the use of other weapons/firearms, such as sniper rifles, machine guns, and incendiary weapons. Additionally, soldiers are trained in hand-to-hand combat and while it won't do much against a high-category Kaiju, it could still come in handy against a smaller monster or offspring. Such training also assists in the soldier's speed, agility, strength, and mental reflexes, which improves their combat abilities overall.

3. GROUND

Artillery: When discussing artillery, we are usually talking about cannons and mortars. Mortars are devices that fire low-velocity projectiles over short distances. These projectiles are typically explosive in nature and can do some serious damage to personnel or lightly-armored targets upon impact. Mortars can also be used to fire other forms of ammunition that serves various strategic uses. Some of these uses include smoke screening/signaling, illumination, or red phosphorus.

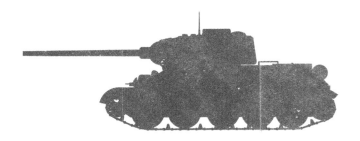

Tanks: The modern-day tank is far different from those used during WWII. Where those tanks varied in protection and movement capabilities, the modern tank, often referred to as the main battle tank (MBT), does not have such vulnerabilities. Introduced during the Cold War, these tanks possess better engines and suspension than their predecessors. Its light armor allows for the firepower of a super-heavy tank (a tank weighing potentially a thousand tons) and the protection of a heavy tank (capable of withstanding large rounds of fire). These modern tanks are our greatest ground defense against any threat. Most tanks are equipped with a tank gun that typically fires between 90 and 130 mm caliber rounds and at least one machine gun, manned by a gunner. These tanks can travel up to 40 mph and traverse most terrain, including sand and mud. The tanks are typically powered by a 1200-1500 hp engine with an operational range of near 310 miles. If need be, the MBT can be made watertight, in order to traverse through small bodies of water and not risk system or personnel damage. The MBT packs a ton of artillery, being able to switch between anti-armor and anti-personnel rounds. The tank also relies on computer systems that help it to identify targets, hazards, or maintenance needs, and can even steady the gun.

Air Defense/Rocket Artillery: Should we need to mount any attack from the ground towards a target in the air, our military is well equipped. Vehicles, such as the M270, are designed to eliminate airborne targets from the ground. These vehicles are equipped with two launch pods, capable of firing up to six missiles each or one warhead. These missiles can reach a firing altitude of up to 164,000 feet and have a range of up to 190 miles. On average, it takes anywhere from 3-4 minutes to reload the missiles. With a slow speed of only 40 mph, the M270 primarily uses a shoot-and-scoot tactic, meaning it will fire from one location and then retreat or move to another so it can reload and attack again.

4. AIR

Fighter Jets: The fighter jets of the modern age represent the ultimate weapon in controlling the battlefield. This is no different when dealing with the Kaiju menace. We possess jets that are capable of delivering devastating damage from both close-range and at a distance. The A10 is an example of a jet capable of extreme damage in air-to-ground scenarios. Capable of reaching almost 520 mph, the A10 was originally designed as an anti-tank aircraft. It possesses a 30mm auto cannon that fires 2100-4200 rounds per minute with a maximum range of 12,000 ft. It also holds rockets/missiles on each wing capable of hitting targets up to 22 miles away. All that, coupled with its impressive plating capable of withstanding armor-piercing rounds, makes the A10 a force to be reckoned with on the battlefield.

If stealth and speed is a necessity, then we need to look no further than the F22 Raptor. This fighter is capable of traveling at 1500 mph without detection. It can fly above 65,000 feet and is capable of hitting a moving target up to 24 miles away. With its impressive speed and versatility, the F22 is one of the best examples in air superiority.

Bombers: Built for durability over speed, these aircraft are designed to cause massive damage to a target area. In the past, bomber aircraft were slow and needed an escort of fighters to defend them. The modern bomber, however, is able to defend itself. Although still not possessing the maneuverability of a fighter jet, modern bombers, such as the B-2, are able to travel great distances without detection. They have built-in systems to avoid radar and ammunition for offensive and defensive purposes. These Bombers are capable of dropping anywhere from 50,000-75,000 pounds of ordinance on a target with near-perfect precision.

Tankers/Cargo: Of course, these high-performance aircraft cannot stay in the air forever. That is where the tanker comes in. Not just for transporting troops and supplies, tankers such as the KC-135 are capable of refueling an aircraft in the air, being able to carry up to 200,000 pounds of extra fuel to help the mission. If we are in need of more troops or even transporting civilians away from danger, the KC-135 can hold up to 80 passengers, helping to ensure the safe travel of many.

Helicopters: Helicopters serve multiple purposes on the battlefield. Although they are not as fast or maneuverable as a fighter jet, these aircraft can still pack a punch. From an offensive standpoint, an Apache helicopter could do massive damage to any target. These flying death machines are equipped with a 30mm chain gun and is capable of firing 995 mph missiles. At an impressive max speed of 176 mph, the Apache is a useful tool in the fight against the Kaiju. There are also cargo helicopters, such as the Chinook. Armed with three medium machine guns and capable of moving over 24,000 pounds, this helicopter is useful for any type of transport. Unlike the fixed-wing aircraft mentioned before, helicopters have the ability to land or takeoff from virtually anywhere. This is especially useful in case you need to make a quick escape and cannot make it to an airport in time.

5. SEA

Aircraft Carrier: Aircraft carriers are one of the most useful resources available to the world's navies. Being able to hold an average of 60 aircraft at a time, these ships act as runways for aircraft departures and arrivals at sea. They are equipped with hangars below deck for aircraft maintenance and have a team of highly-qualified professionals to work on them. These air carriers are powered by nuclear reactors, giving them impressive endurance at sea. They only need to return to port for supplies. Most carriers also have 3-4 missile launchers, capable of hitting a target miles away. In case of a submerged attack, these vessels possess chaff and flares that can be fired to disrupt any hostile artillery fired their way.

Destroyers: These warships are the tanks of the sea. Designed for a multitude of missions, destroyers possess radar defenses, surface-to-air artillery, and antisubmarine capabilities. These warships can be powered by both gas turbines and nuclear power, and they can travel up to a range of 4,400 nautical miles before needing to refuel. Destroyers possess an extensive artillery and can fire Tomahawk missiles at a target as far as 1,550 miles away. Each destroyer can be upgraded based on the mission it is assisting with and is one of the most diverse nautical weapons ever created.

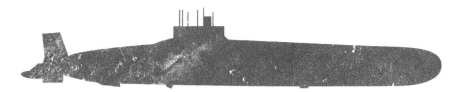

Submarines: Submarines are vessels capable of traveling both above and underwater. They are primarily designed for underwater combat and can reach depths as low as 950 feet in a tested environment. These nuclear-powered vessels are capable of being out at sea for up to 90 days before needing to resupply. Due to the power of their nuclear reactors, these submarines do not need to refuel for up to 30 years. Although the full extent of the weaponry on board is kept secret, these underwater vessels possess an impressive array of weapons capable of hitting land and sea target from miles away.

6. SPACE

The environment of outer space is home to satellites, some of mankind's most impressive inventions. These satellites have the uncanny ability to connect mankind in ways we never thought possible. We can use them to relay messages, provide surveillance, and in theory, as a weapon. We have been able to equip space stations and even some satellites with weapons in the past, but only as a defensive measure against perceived threats from other countries. In fact, during the Cold War, the Soviet Union developed a weapons system in orbit that would have been capable of dropping a nuclear warhead from low orbit. Luckily, this never came to be, and the program was scrapped after the collapse of the Soviet Union. During the period of 1972-1979, the United States and the Soviet Union developed the SALT II treaty. This treaty's main purpose was to limit the nuclear arsenal of both countries. It also explicitly forbade the use of nuclear weaponry in the space environment. This treaty has been agreed upon by other nations as well. So when we wonder about the defenses we possess in outer space, the short answer is none. We can always equip satellites and space stations with weaponry, but as of right now, no space craft is equipped with such technology, and doing so would be in direct violation of the treaty created by man.

TERRAIN TACTICS

This section talks about the strategies used by the military when fighting the Kaiju. The tactics used are ultimately determined by the type of Kaiju and its location. We have spent most of this chapter giving an overview of some of mankind's greatest weapons, so now we will explain how they are used.

1. LAND

The military is most equipped to deal with an attack on land. Military forces around the world possess multiple land vehicles, troops, aircraft, and even warships capable of hitting a target on the ground. The first priority for the military would be to keep the Kaiju away from populated areas and dangerous locations such as nuclear power plants.

To do this, the military would use its multiple tanks and surface-to-air vehicles to fire at the Kaiju. They would attempt to guide it, or at the very least make it keep its distance from the protected target. The vehicles would set up a safe distance from the Kaiju so that they can avoid immediate contact. This will be tricky in some areas, as Kaiju can travel great distances in a single step. The vehicles would also be escorted by many troops on the ground. These troops would split their time equally between protecting civilians and escorting the military vehicles. Although they could engage the monster, most service rifles will do little damage and only serve to agitate it. Should the Kaiju get close to the ground vehicles, it will most likely decimate them, so it is important for them to keep their distance and wear the creature down.

Fighter jets and other aircraft will also be able to attack the Kaiju. As long as the aircraft keep their distance, they should be able to avoid harm. If the Kaiju has any projectile abilities, allowing it to hit targets from a distance, then it would be wise to attack it using a bomber from a high altitude or, if close to the coast, a destroyer armed with missiles.

2. AIR

A Kaiju in the air possesses one of the greatest dangers to mankind. These Kaiju are typically very fast and have a much wider range of attack than their counterparts. In order to fight such creatures, the military would have to work together as a group. The air support needed to take out an Aero Kaiju would be immense, with a whole flight of aircraft required to attack the Kaiju from a distance. Additionally, the Air Force would need to use air-to-ground vehicles to fire at the airborne Kaiju and attempt to weaken or kill it. This will require the fighters to keep their distance from the creature to avoid friendly fire. If those methods prove to be unsuccessful, then the only other method available would be suicide attacks, but these are only to be used as a last resort.

3. SEA

The ocean is a complex battlefield. We possess multiple nautical weapons and vehicles to dispose of the lower category Kaiju. The problem we face is the attraction these beasts have to our nuclear-powered vehicles. As stated above, most Kaiju are attracted nuclear energy. The KRSD believes this energy is what powers them and in many ways, created them in the first place. Unfortunately, this piece of information wasn't discovered until after we had built these nuclear-powered vessels.

These vessels have proved very effective against the Kaiju and in some cases, have been used to our advantage. Kaiju have been more likely to attack these vessels then shipping freighters, even if the freighter has a large supply of fish. The Kaiju is then soundly dispatched by the impressive artillery these ships have. The debate to get rid of this power source has been argued relentlessly, but as of the writing this book, we are still using nuclear-powered vessels to fight the Kaiju menace.

4. SPACE

As stated above, we have no way to attack a Kaiju from space. Due to the treaties our world leaders have in place, we are unable to equip our satellites or space stations with any such artillery. If a Kaiju should ever emerge from outer space, we would be unable to attack it using our satellites. This could be very hazardous, as a satellite that is knocked out of orbit would do massive damage to the earth's surface. We could only hope it would land in a non-populated area.

Should the Kaiju get close to the Earth's atmosphere, we do possess ground-based weapons that could be fired upon the Kaiju. These weapons could potentially do more harm than good, however. If they were to miss the target and hit another satellite, then we could cause just as much damage as the Kaiju. Hopefully, the Kaiju would eventually land on Earth, allowing us to eliminate it using one of the tactics listed earlier.

It would unfortunately take an attack like this to allow the leaders of the world to begin building space defense against all threats. In theory, we could eventually develop a weapon that would allow us to attack from space, allowing us to keep our troops at a safer distance when dispatching the Kaiju. These developments, however, are a ways off.

NUCLEAR THREAT

If a Kaiju were to appear with nuclear capability, it would create many challenges for the military that we have never faced before. A Kaiju capable of emitting nuclear energy, whether through concentrated blasts or sporadic bursts, would cause massive destruction as it moves from one area to the next.

The use of ground troops would be basically nonexistent due to radiation. The only troops on the ground would be the ones operating the vehicles. The KRSD believes that these Category V Kaiju would be primarily interested in collecting more nuclear energy. This means that instead of traveling to areas high in population, they would instead go towards nuclear reactors. The military would attempt to redirect the creature from the most populated areas using lower grade weapons designed to harm but not kill. After getting the Kaiju far enough away from civilization, the military would then move to heavy artillery in an attempt to kill the creature.

These Kaiju would essentially be a walking nuclear reactor. Any weapon powerful enough to kill it would potentially cause a nuclear fallout for that area. Should the military use a nuclear weapon against the Kaiju, it is unknown if it would cause a fallout or if the Kaiju would somehow be able to absorb the blast and become more powerful in the process. A creature capable of controlling nuclear energy defies all logic known to mankind. It would use nuclear fission as a natural bodily function. Something this terrifying would be a walking doomsday scenario waiting to happen.

ELECTROMAGNETIC PULSE

A Kaiju capable of emitting an electromagnetic pulse (EMP) possesses just as much, if not more, complications then a nuclear threat, as it could potentially shut down the majority of our arsenal.

An EMP varies in power and depending on its strength, will do anything from jam radio transmissions to completely fry all electronic equipment within a specific radius. This could be hazardous on any level, since no radio transmissions means difficulty communicating on the battlefield. If a Kaiju were to appear with EMP abilities, it could potentially stop missiles, jets, tanks, and any other weapons or vehicles run by electricity. Over the years, the U.S. (and most of the world) has developed a military force dependent on technology. It has near infinite capabilities on the battlefield, but these capabilities are virtually nonexistent against a Kaiju capable of emitting high-level EMP fields. Although it is unlikely a Kaiju could ever possess such power as to knock missiles out of the sky, it is something we must prepare for. This Kaiju would have to be dealt with from a distance, with the only close attacks done with automatic weapons. Ground forces should use maximum caution when approaching such a creature, especially in an urban environment. EMP fields are normally harmless to humans, but when around metal such as pipes or support beams (everything a city is made out of), these fields can be redirected and channeled directly to one target, amplifying it in the process.

The worst-case scenario is an Aero Class Kaiju with low-high range EMP capabilities. This Kaiju would essentially be untouchable, having the literal ability to knock aircraft out of the air. The only weapons we would be able to use are the ground-to-air artillery. The hope would be that the Kaiju wouldn't be to dodge all the missiles or that it would not go after the vehicles/silos launching such attacks. A Kaiju with EMP capabilities would require some creative military strategy in order to dispatch it.

GLACIER BAY

Seattle, Washington

It is a cold November morning in the Port of Seattle. The sky is dark gray, and it is even beginning to snow a little bit. I see Norman Rafferty, who is waiting for me by the Glacier Bay Memorial. This memorial, which lies in the middle of Seattle fish market, was built to commemorate the passengers and crew of the Winter's Jewel cruise ship. This ship was one of the first major Kaiju attacks on a luxury cruise liner. What makes this attack so unique is the fact that it happened in such a cold climate. Norman is one of only a handful of passengers who survived the ordeal. A tall and slender man who is already wearing his winter attire, Norman greets me with a handshake and a smile. He smartly suggests that we enjoy some of Seattle's seafood while we conduct the interview.

It wasn't nearly this cold when we set out on our cruise. Mom worked at the newspaper and Dad was a teacher. One day, she surprised us with an all expenses paid Alaskan cruise that she had won at work.

We were ecstatic, to say the least. I had never been on a cruise before and Alaska seemed like a blast. To make it even better, it was in the summertime, so we wouldn't be limited on which excursions we could do. Of course I was just excited for the unlimited amounts of ice cream.

Were there ever any thoughts or worry of a possible Kaiju attack?

No. We had seen the stories on the news, everyone had at that point, but besides that incident in Canada, no one had ever seen a Kaiju this far up north. As long as we weren't sailing any place tropical, we figured that we were okay. Even today, what happened to us and to the Canadians, it's still considered abnormal. Kaiju hate the cold, we all know that, and the rare ones that don't are covered head to tail in fur. We had lived in Seattle for a long time, seen plenty of ships come and go from the port, and had no issues. We had a few Kaiju spotted off the coast, but never an attack. So there was no concern from us. I'd say the cruise line felt the same way, because they barely had any anti-Kaiju defenses on board. Given the amount of cruise ships attacked in the last 10 years though, I don't think those defenses make much of a difference anyways.

Our ship sailed out Monday morning. We were at sea for a day and a half before we got to our first port. I spent that first day playing my handheld games and enjoying the ice cream. My parents spent a little bit of time in the casino and at the bar. They were pretty lax with worrying about me. I was a 14 year old kid on a cruise. Unless I got thrown overboard somehow, I wasn't going too far. I couldn't really blame them for being so carefree. It was a perfect time for a vacation. Mom and Dad had both been putting in a lot of overtime lately. They were fighting a lot before the cruise about bills or other things, so it was good to see them happy and relaxed. Those first few days went off without issue. On the third day, we sailed out of Ketchikan. Everything still seemed fairly normal. Later that night is when things started to becoming more and more uneasy. The water had been calm the entire trip, but for whatever reason from

Ketchikan to our next destination of Glacier Bay, the seas were very uneasy. All of that ice cream I had eaten was coming back to bite me in the ass. I was spending most of the time either throwing up in the bathroom or over the edge of the ship. It was raining a lot as well. I don't mean just a small drizzle either. It was a torrential downpour. We weren't even allowed on deck during the worst of it.

Did they try to turn the ship around?

I don't remember them making any sort of announcement like that. I think they were hoping the waters would calm down once we got into Glacier Bay. Although it was unusual weather, they still weren't to panicking. It wasn't like the ship was in any danger of capsizing. The waves were just enough to make the passengers feel uneasy. We spent the majority of that day in our room, only venturing out to get some food. I was guzzling down some ginger ale after some of the staff suggested it would help upset stomachs. I don't think I've ever drank so much ginger ale in my life, but it still didn't seem to help. My parents took the day off from their drunken adventures to take care of me. Although I would still get up on occasion to throw up, I was able to get some sleep that night, but it didn't last long. Sometime in the early hours of the morning, maybe 2 or 3 AM, we woke up to a sudden impact. The ship had hit something, something very large, and it was enough to knock all of us from our beds. The PA system turned on immediately following this. Our captain apologized for the inconvenience, but it appeared we had had a small collision. He assured us that nothing was wrong however and to stay in our rooms until further confirmation.

Were you nervous at all during this?

Incredibly nervous. It had been a hell of a day to begin with, and being thrown out of bed didn't make it any better. To make things more uneasy, the cruise staff could be heard running around in the hallways. They seemed very panicked and although they weren't speaking English, I could tell this situation had them on edge. My parents weren't nearly as worried, or at least they didn't seem to be. I remember Dad saying that we had probably just hit a small iceberg and that it was nothing to worry about. It's called Glacier Bay for a reason, he said. He then made a Titanic joke to try and calm the mood, but Mom told him to shut up. We waited in our room for what seemed like forever before the next call came over the PA. It was the captain again. He once again assured us that there was no need to panic but that he would like everyone to begin reporting to their mustering stations should the need arise for evacuation. Things were still pretty calm at this point, but that didn't last very long. We had begun to walk down our hallway to our mustering station when the ship began to shake. It was subtle at first. It felt a lot like the rumble of a car engine when its starting up on a cold day. People didn't react at first, it was honestly very hard to move with how much the ship was shaking, but that changed when we started to hear scraping at one side of the ship. It sounded like something was trying to claw its way in. This caused a panic almost instantly.

How close were you to the lifeboats?

Not close enough. It's funny. When you first get on the cruise ship, you spend the first hour or so going over all of the safety procedures. It's annoying and tedious, but for the most part, the instructions are fairly simple. Each person is assigned to a mustering area depending on which part of the ship they are staying in. During an emergency, you report to your mustering station, be safely loaded into the lifeboats, and evacuated by the cruise staff. That's not what happened, though. As soon as people started hearing the Kaiju clawing at the side of the ship, all protocol went out the window. Passenger and cruise worker alike were all stampeding towards the lifeboats. There was no order, no reasoning, just fear. At one point, I tripped and fell to the floor. No one even seemed to notice, no matter how loudly I yelled for help. Everyone just kept running, trampling over top of me as they went. I just covered my face and head and hoped to God that no one would crush me. I was sure that I was going to suffocate or be trampled to death.

The next thing I knew, my father's hand reached down and grabbed me, pulling me up by the collar of the shirt. He was able to push against the stampede of people and get to me before anything serious happened. He slung me over his shoulders and began to march back towards my mother. I remember being so independent at 14, thinking that I had life all figured out and that I was more of an adult than my parents, but in that instance, I was just a scared little boy.

We eventually made it to the lifeboats, where the situation was more chaotic. People were fighting each other to get on these boats. There was no order to anything. It didn't matter if you were a man, woman, or child, Only the most aggressive were getting on these lifeboats. I wish I could say that I was calm during all of this, but that wasn't the case. We joined the mob of people as soon as we got to the lifeboats. I remember my parents and me screaming, just like everyone else, demanding to be let on the boat. At one point, a man pushed my mother and Dad grabbed him by the shirt collar, ready to throw down. Luckily, before anything escalated further, a crew member fired his gun in the air. You know? That stereotypical scene that you see in any movie where people are arguing and one guy needs to get everyone's attention. Turns out, it's a pretty damn good attention-getter. He was able to calm us all down and get people into the lifeboats in an orderly fashion. The man that had previously shoved my mother had apologized and it seemed like everyone was beginning to act like people again. We got into the lifeboats and began to lower ourselves into the water.

Was the ship still shaking?

Yes, the Kaiju was hitting the backside of the ship with everything it had, just looking for a weak spot. Between that and the freezing cold, we were fucked. We were only a few miles away from Glacier Bay and even though it was the summertime, it was still freezing. Many of us, my family included, didn't think to put anything on other than our pajamas. Of course, we stopped paying attention to the cold when we heard the Kaiju for the first time. They were lowering our raft down the side of the boat when we first heard it. A roar came from the other side of the ship, followed by panicked chatter over the lifeboat captain's intercom. I remember someone screaming, "Oh my God, it's starboard. Oh my God, it's coming for the boat." This thing barreled into the ship from the side opposite of us. Our life raft, which was still loading some passengers, was knocked loose from its harness and we began to propel down into the water. I hugged my mother and screamed as loud as I could. I was praying, praying that we would just get away from this boat. We landed hard into the water and without hesitation, the captain began driving away from the cruise ship.

Did you ever see the Kaiju that attacked the boat?

Not at first. It was nighttime, and those life rafts do not have great visibility to begin with. On top of that, there was over 200 of us crammed into a raft that was probably only meant for 150 people, so it was hard to see. That didn't stop us from trying, though. We were all were looking out the back windows, trying to get a glimpse of what was happening to the cruise ship. At first, we didn't see anything except for the fact that the ship was still being rammed into. After almost 15 minutes of this, we saw the ship erupt in flames. That's when we saw the Kaiju illuminated for the first time. It was only for a few seconds, but that was plenty to get a good look at it. It had these piercing yellow eyes and its face was all squishy, like a squid or something. It looked like we were being attacked by something out of an HP Lovecraft novel. I saw the creature wrap its body around the ship, almost bending it in half as he pulled it down under the sea.

It was quiet for a while after that. The captain of our life boat was a Filipino guy. He kept referring to himself as Captain Marty, but I don't think that was his real name. He was the same man who fired the gun into the air and attempted to calm everyone down. Captain Marty was trying to radio for help with the Coast Guard but wasn't having much luck. I'm guessing the other lifeboats were doing the same, but we didn't have much communication with them. It was dark, but if I had to guess, I would say almost 12 lifeboats were able to get off the boat in time before it was pulled under.

How long were you adrift before help came?

We were floating out there for almost three hours. We huddled together for warmth and waited for someone to come help us. Like I said earlier, we had about 12 life rafts that escaped the initial attack, but by the time the Coast Guard got there, only four of them remained.

What happened to the others?

My guess is that they got pulled under like the cruise ship. It was dark, and the waves and wind were drowning out almost all other noise at sea. Usually the life rafts would huddle together in order to make rescue efforts easier, but considering it was a Kaiju attack, I guess the standard practice is to spread out. The less huddled together you are, the less likely a target you appear to be to the monsters. We didn't hear any of the other rafts get attacked, but there wasn't any trace of them left. I remember being so relieved when I finally saw the Coast Guard choppers that I started to cry. I'm talking ugly cry face with snot coming out of everywhere. That's how happy I was to see them. It took some time, but they were eventually able to get all of us into the helicopters and the fuck away from Glacier Bay. For us, the nightmare was over. But for military, it had just started.

THE STORM

Lake Tahoe, California

After a few hours of driving along the coast and off the winding mountain road, I am greeted at the entrance to the Lake Tahoe National Park by James Madsen. James and his friends were some of the eyewitnesses to the infamous Kaiju attack in 2012. James drives us a little further up the mountain until we get to a point marked off with a 'no trespassing' sign. It is here that we decide to get out of our vehicles and walk the trails. After almost an hour of hiking, we arrive to what looks like it was once a beautiful cabin. The only thing seemingly intact in this area is a small picnic table that we sit down at and begin our interview.

Believe it or not, this cabin used to be quite a cozy little spot. My friends and I had been coming here for 10 years or so. It started back when my buddy Marcus and his family invited myself and our other friends, Dakota and Jeff. Ever since then, this trip was a yearly tradition. Over the years, we had a few additions to our little group, with

Marcus getting married, me getting engaged, Dakota having a girl-friend, and Jeff being in a very intimate relationship with his right hand. [laughs] That year was the 10th anniversary of our first camping trip. No matter what was going on in life, we could always count on this trip. Lately, though, it had been a lot harder to stay in touch with these guys. People change, and life starts to take over. It wasn't made any easier by the fact that all four of us were spread out all over the country. Marcus was the only one that stayed near our hometown. Him and his longtime girlfriend Shirley had settled down and gotten married just a couple years prior. Jeff was working for a consulting firm, and Dakota had taken a job in Colorado as a lawyer. Personally, I had told my then fiancée, now wife, Jennifer that I thought this would be the last trip that we would make together. I joined the Air Force a few years back and we were stationed in North Dakota. About the complete opposite of California. This trip, along with the added issues of work and planning a wedding, had been a pain in the ass to say the least.

How long did this trip typically last?

We would get here on the weekend and stay the whole week usually. Despite the pain in the ass that it was to prepare for the trip, once we were here, it was a great way to relax and get back to nature. We would spend the week fishing and rafting by a nearby river. When I say fishing, I really mean just drinking by the river and casting our line into the water. We rarely ever caught anything. We would play board games, sit by the campfire at night, drink, and tell stories, remembering the days of high school or catching everyone up to speed on the most interesting facts of each other's lives. One thing we always did was put our cell phones into a small jewelry box in the cabin and shut them in there. We started doing this as a way to truly escape everything for the week. This way, everyone wasn't focused on the outside world or posting to social media. Our time here was meant not just to see everyone, but to also recharge, something I think camping is great for. Of course, we weren't without our phones the whole week. Everyone could grab them before bed, but not while we were up and socializing. Jennifer even went as far as to get a Polaroid camera for the trip. This way, there was truly no excuse to be on our phones. We didn't have any TV up there, but we did have a radio. We always had it on but hardly ever kept it tuned to the same station. We would take turns cycling through the stations, trying to find something to listen to. All the frustrations I had before the trip had disappeared. I was in nature with the people I cared for the most and away from all of life's stressors. Life was good, or at least it was for the first couple of days. Before we started to get on each other's nerves...

I think towards the third day, everyone in our camping party was starting to get a little annoyed with each other. Us guys had been coming up here for the last few years. We loved to camp and if one of us was bugging the other, then we would just go our separate ways and do something on our own for a couple of hours. This was no issue to us, but I think Shirley in particular was not a fan of camping. She was nice enough in social settings, but I think she was ready to go home. Her attitude about the trip was starting to affect other people's fun time. This led to some friction between the members of the group. On the morning of the third day, I don't think any of the couples had really interacted with each other since dinner the night prior. Me and Jenny were relaxing in our room, where she was taking pictures of the Polaroid photos she had printed off earlier and then posting them to social media. We did that until Marcus came and got us for a fishing trip. We hadn't been fishing yet on that trip and I think Marcus was hoping that was just the thing that we needed to help everyone relax. More importantly, I think he was hoping it would help Shirley relax. Marcus was, for lack of a better term, the leader of our group. He wasn't the smartest or the most athletic, but he just had a way about him that made you want to follow him. I think he had a good handle on the group and knew how to bring us together. So, we got all of our fishing gear and swimsuits and left the cabin. Marcus was taking us to a farther spot that he said had better fishing. It was about an hour to hike there, but once we were there, it was worth it. We spent the rest of the time fishing and relaxing by the water. Even Shirley's attitude seemed to change, with the help of one or five cups of wine. It was sunny when we first set out for this fishing trip, with no signs of that changing. The forecast called for clear skies all day, so when the skies started to get dark all of a sudden, we decided to cut the trip short and go back to the cabin.

It started to storm?

No, but it was starting to look nasty out. The clear skies we were enjoying had disappeared and were replaced with storm clouds. Although it didn't rain by us, we could hear the thunder in the distance. We were a good distance away from the coast but high enough in the mountains to see any weather coming our way. It reminded me of the storms we used to get when we were kids, but I didn't think it would be that bad due to what time of year was. In fact, the only thing that seemed odd at the time was the birds. After the first few sounds of thunder, all the birds in the trees began to fly away, almost at once. This was kind of creepy, but at the time, we just thought it was them trying to get away from the storm. Our plan was to go back to the cabin, listen to the radio, finish the alcohol, and check our phones for weather and see how bad it was supposed to get that night. Truth be told, I don't think anyone really minded the rain, most of the group being pretty tipsy at the moment. We were also a little preoccupied singing and dancing to some of our favorite 80s songs. We walked down the path having our own singing competition to pass the time. It wasn't until we were a few feet from the cabin that we started to hear the emergency broadcast.

Over the loudspeaker?

No, over the radio that we left sitting on this picnic table. It was eerie to say the least. All these things that happened so suddenly seemed so natural to us. We really paid no attention to them, but when you add in the emergency broadcast, everything becomes much more terrifying. I remember that we were walking down the path towards our cabin. Shirley and Jenny were in front of us, they were singing a duet and getting very into their performance. I was close behind, trying not to get roped into the performance. As we started to approach, we heard the broadcast and the girls' singing started to trail off. I don't know what it is about that broadcast that is so creepy. Maybe it's the fact that it causes everyone around you to suddenly become silent or the anticipation of waiting to find out what the emergency is. I just remember feeling very on edge when we started to hear everything. We were far away still, but I could hear the radio announcer's voice over the broadcast signal. I only heard a broken transmission of, *"This is...emergency broadcast...inclement weather..."*As we got closer, we were then able to hear the transmission in its entirety.

"Warning, this is not a test. This is an emergency broadcast from the national disaster organization. There is a weather warning for severe winds, rain, and other types of inclement weather for the Grand Bay area. All residents are advised to take shelter and secure any outdoor belong-ings. Warning, this is not a test..."

And then it just trailed off and began to repeat itself. Most of the group wanted to stick with our original plan, wait out the storm in the safety of the cabin and drink the rest of the booze, but I felt uneasy for some reason. The birds leaving as we were walking back was creepy enough, but the suddenness of the storm just had me on edge. I went to the back of the cabin along the hill to see the storm approaching from the coast. The skies were gray by us but over the water, they were pitch black. The lightning was intense, and thunder was rumbling. The thunder sounded strange though, like it was unnatural. Every time I would hear the rumblings, there was some other noise that preceded it. I watched that coastline for a good while, waiting for something to happen. It wasn't until the next lightning strike that I finally saw it. When the lightning struck, the black clouds lit up, illuminating the inside of the storm like Christmas tree. One part of the clouds stayed dark, though. With every flash of lightning, the shadow in the clouds would appear in a different location. It reminded me of really bad claymation, because of how choppy it was. It wasn't until the third or fourth flash of lightning that I got a better look at this "shadow." It had wings, it had a face, and it had a very distinct set of emerald green eyes. At this point, I realized what was flying around in the clouds—a Kaiju. I was running up the hill screaming for everyone to get their stuff because we needed to leave. The rest of the group, however, just looked at me in drunken confusion. I'm sure to them it looked like their friend James was having some type of PTSD episode. I was nervously trying to describe what I saw to my friends while at the same time trying to load up the vehicles. Looking back at it, I don't think that I was even grabbing anything specific. I think I was just running in and out of the cabin throwing random Items into my truck. Needless to say, this did not create the most flattering image to the group. Eventually, they were able to settle me down enough so I could better explain what I saw. I recounted in as much detail as I could, but I don't think any of them, including Jenny, really believed that what I saw was true.

What changed your minds?

We heard it. Everyone was talking to me, trying to calm me down by telling me I was acting crazy. This, shockingly enough, had the opposite effect for calming me down. As they were doing that, a particularly loud sound of thunder went off in the background. The thunder was followed by what I can only describe as a loud screeching noise, like something from an animal. As soon as we heard that, the whole group ran to the overlook and saw the storm clouds moving overhead. With every flash of lightning, we could see the shadow creature that I was rambling about. It was still only shadows at first, but as the thunder got louder and more constant, we started to realize that it wasn't thunder we were hearing. A giant bat-like creature emerged from the storm. Each flap of its wings brought a thunderous sound with it. I think for the first few seconds, we were all frozen in fear and then almost in unison ran back to the cabin to load up the vehicles and get the fuck out of there.

Was it flying towards you guys?

No... Actually... I don't know...

I just know that as soon as we saw the thing, we panicked and any training I had to deal with Kaiju—which was very limited, mind you--didn't cover what to do if one of these fuckers could fly. The only thing it did cover is when these things appear, you want to be as far away from the coast as possible. My first and only thought was to get us the hell off this mountain and drive as far away as possible. Oddly enough, the only person that thought we should stay at the cabin was Shirley, who seemed so adamant about leaving just a few hours ago. Much to her dismay though, the rest of the group had made their decision. In between loading up the vehicles, I would check to see where the Kaiju was, if it had flown any closer or if it was flying towards us specifically, but I couldn't see anything. Whatever storm was following this thing had crept in with it and made it almost impossible to see the city along the coast. The only thing that was visible were a few very tall buildings. We heard a lot of noise from below but nothing we could decipher aside from some sirens and what sounded like a few explosions. I'm not sure if anything was actually blowing up or if it was all in my head. It was also hard to tell what noise was created by the storm and what was created by the creature.

How long before you were actually driving down the mountain?

From us seeing the creature to getting in the vehicles, I'd say it was under 10 minutes. I jumped in my truck with Jenny and Jeff while the others went into Marcus's jeep. I was in the front of our frightened little convoy and Marcus was following closely behind. We couldn't have gotten more than a mile down the mountain when I heard what sounded like the loudest thunder I have ever heard, followed by what felt like an earthquake. I assumed that something large had crashed into the side of the mountain, I hoped it was the creature. Maybe it had been shot down, I told myself. Whatever caused the rumble lit a fire under my ass and if I wasn't speeding down the mountain already, I sure as hell was now. Marcus was still keeping pace but wasn't able to go quite as fast as me. We eventually made it down the mountain and onto the highway, which was chaotic to say the least. There weren't as many cars as you'd think there'd be. I'm guessing with the suddenness of the Kaiju and the strange weather that not many people were able to get on the road in time. Even with few people, it was still dangerous. Apparently when there is a natural disaster, all normal rules of the road do not apply. We had people doing all sorts of crazy things that they thought would help them get to safety faster. The reality is, though, it caused many people to get into accidents and created chaos where the Kaiju wasn't.

Where was the Kaiju during all of this?

We honestly weren't sure. At first, I thought he was in the mountains where we had just left, but as we got down onto the highway and looped around, we didn't see him. What we did see was what caused that rumble during our initial escape. Apparently, the bat had somehow thrown a city bus into the side of the mountain. This led to a small rockslide that had landed on the highway, creating some obstacles for us to drive around. Eventually, we were able to get away from the mountains and onto the open road. I think we all hoped that the danger had passed, but just as we started to feel safe, a fog started to creep in behind us. One by one, vehicles started to disappear in the fog. I am usually a very safe driver, but during this time, I was pushing on the gas pedal as hard as I could, but it seemed to do no good. I saw Marcus's jeep disappear behind us and then the fog started gaining on us. It seemed to consume my truck in an almost paranormal way. The next thing I remember was that my truck was launched into the air and then blackness.

Launched? As in thrown?

No, I didn't feel anything grab onto my vehicle. It felt like a strong gust of wind hit us. We flipped through the air for a few seconds before coming down hard on our side. I don't know how long I was knocked out for, but eventually, I came to. I checked on Jenny, who was still unconscious but breathing. Jeff wasn't so lucky, though. My best guess is that he wasn't wearing his seatbelt and when we flipped, he rag-dolled in the backseat until we finally stopped. What was left of Jeff was half in the backseat and the other half slung over the rear window.

I started to get myself and Jenny out of the truck. I tried waking her a few times, but she was out cold. This wasn't anything that I was trained how to do or anything like that. I think I was just in survival mode at this point. I knew I had to get her away from the truck in case it caught fire or anything. I wasn't focused on the creature or the fog or anything else, I was just focused on getting Jenny to safety. Once I dragged us out of there, I went back to check on Jeff, just in case there was something else I could do. During this, I noticed a bone was sticking out of my arm. Honest to God, I hadn't noticed until that point. Everything hurt and my adrenaline was going so much that nothing really registered. I think seeing my bones stick out gave me a quick dose of reality and snapped me out of whatever shock I was in. Suddenly, I was very aware of my surroundings.

Did you see Marcus and the others?

Not at first. First, I was looking around the road. I didn't see any other survivors walking around besides myself, but I did see some other vehicles that had been flipped. It didn't look like the other passengers had any better luck than poor Jeff. The fog had started to lift but only slightly. I still couldn't see more than maybe 15 feet in front of me. I started to hear glass breaking and thought it was someone else trying to kick out their windshield. I started to hobble towards that noise, thinking that it might be Marcus and the others. As I started to get closer, I was becoming more and more aware of my injuries with every movement. The only thing that was keeping me going during all this was that I needed to help my friends. I was so relieved when I got to the source of the noise and saw Marcus's jeep. It was almost like God wanted me to find it. I remember there was a single ray of sunshine that somehow broke through the fog and was shining on the jeep.

It sounds like a miracle.

It turned out to be more of a nightmare. As I walked up to the jeep, I saw Marcus's body laying in the road. He seemed unconscious, but I could tell that he was breathing. It looked like I was right—he had broken out his windshield and crawled out. I started moving faster towards him and once I got close enough, I reached out to grab him. But as I did, Marcus was pulled into the fog. I watched in horror as the Kaiju emerged from behind Marcus's jeep. The sunlight gave me a clear view of the creature as it scarfed down poor, defenseless Marcus. The Kaiju had almost reptilian skin and was different shades of black and gray. Besides its skin, the rest of its body resembled a vampire bat. Its eyes were a deep emerald green and it looked like it had shark teeth. It also had spikes along its back, almost like a porcupine.

What did you do?

Are you kidding me? I couldn't do anything. Seeing this thing took me right back into shock. I was absolutely frozen in fear. I don't even think I remembered to breathe. I just stood there in disbelief that such a nightmare could exist and that not only did it exist, but it had just killed two of my best friends. Unfortunately for me, he was not as awestruck by my appearance. I saw his nostrils start to flare, like he caught the scent of something that interested him. Then he immediately looked down at me. I remember hoping that this thing's vision was based only on movement, so I tried to keep very still. Of course, I knew my masterful plan had failed when the Kaiju looked right at me and growled. He had just found his next meal and wasn't about to let it get away. I turned around to hobble away as fast as I could. As I started to retreat, I heard what sounded like a crushing noise coming from behind me. When I turned around to see the creature, it was gone, but Marcus's jeep had been caved in. I turned back around, only to be greeted by a mouth of sharp teeth glaring at me. The creature had jumped in front of me, cutting me off from Jenny and the truck. He had me cornered. "This is it," I thought. "I'm fucked."

I don't remember backing up, but the next thing I knew, my back was pressed up against the jeep and the creature was stalking towards me. The last thing I saw was the Kaiju open its mouth, ready to have another highway snack. I closed my eyes, hoping it would be as painless as possible, when suddenly I heard machine gun fire followed by the painful shrieks from the bat. I opened my eyes to see that something had shot the creature in the back. The sound of jets flying overhead was music to my ears as I looked up to see the formation flying past us. The creature let out a sickening scream and flapped its thunderous wings. It was pissed and it was going after the jet that hit it. The bat took off towards the jet, disappearing into the clouds. I heard what I thought was thunder again, only to see more jets racing towards the Kaiju. I collapsed against the jeep. I remember feeling sorry for the Kaiju. It had no idea about the fight it was in for.

KAIJU VS. GIANT ROBOTS

MECHS

The Kaiju are creatures unlike anything we have seen before. These hulking monstrosities show up at random, attacking valuable resources and ending countless lives. Although they are eventually stopped, the damage they are able to inflict in such a short amount of time outweighs that of any army mankind has ever created. Even when facing the Kaiju, the military's goal is to attack it and get it as far away from civilians and resources as possible, but this takes time and can lead to more collateral damage. Our tactics are limited by our military weapons and vehicles, which, although useful, cannot outperform the Kaiju when it comes to power. But what if they did? What if we possessed a weapon powerful enough that we could match the Kaiju's might, meeting them head-on in battle?

This is where the concept of giant robots comes into play. If you ask any child who watches cartoons, the idea is an obvious one. Build a giant robot (mech) to battle the Kaiju and beat it senseless. These mechs could be equipped with the most impressive arsenal we have at our disposal and could overpower the Kaiju. These metal behemoths could physically force the Kaiju back, taking the battle away from populated areas. This would give the military some time to secure the area and evacuate, while the Kaiju is focused on the immediate threat and not its food.

Although concept seems like a good idea on paper, and it could be, the implementation of building a small army of mechs possesses many issues

1. Movement

When you think about it, the human form is an amazing design for movement. We are able to walk and run on virtually any terrain and thanks to our hands and feet, we are also very capable climbers. This makes the human form an attractive one when building a mech capable of outmaneuvering the Kaiju menace. We often forget one key thing, however, and that is that walking can be very hard.

The concept of walking is difficult, as we are essentially making sure we don't fall forward by putting one leg after the other in front of ourselves. Eventually, we learn how to do this and gain some balance in the process and before you know it, we have mastered walking. While this isn't quite as difficult for a human, it is incredibly difficult for a machine. Creating a machine capable of bipedal (two-legged) movement faces two key obstacles we must first overcome. We could make bipedal mechs right now if we wanted, but they would not function as desired. A mech that moves on two legs would create a stiletto effect, putting most of its weight on a small area. This isn't as big of a deal on solid ground, but if a mech were to move in loose terrain, the ground may not be able to support it, causing it to sink. Another issue a bipedal mech faces is all of its weight being put on its lower joints. This creates a lot of strain on the joints and could lead to difficulty maneuvering. Over time, the weight would add increasing pressure to the mech, causing it to break down faster if overexerted.

The second issue facing a bipedal mech is balance. As humans, we are able to balance ourselves thanks to a combination of multiple body systems working together, such as sight, sound, and touch. For a machine, this would be very difficult. Much of the mech's computer systems would be dedicated strictly to movement. Other large vehicles, such as cruise ships, have overcome this issue by using a gyroscope in order to stay afloat, however, walking is very unstable. The taller an object is, the harder it is to balance. This in turn would make the mech slower due to its need for balance. We are making strides in this field but for now, scientists and engineers seem to be abandoning a bipedal system in favor of wheeled locomotion similar to a tank. While it is not the most maneuverable or fastest form of movement, it is a starting point we can continue to advance from in the field of robotics.

2. Power Source

Once we tackle the issue of movement, we must then ask ourselves how we would power such a large machine. Power in the lab is one thing, because the mechs are either plugged into a power source or the scientists are able to replace its batteries as it goes. These resources would most likely not be available in the field. It would take more than a normal battery to power a 50-100 feet tall machine that uses state of the art weaponry and detection systems. So, scientists are looking at other sources.

The first source considered was solar power, however, this would give off less power than a battery and should only be used as a last resort. Solar power is not always a reliable source either, depending on the weather or location.

Scientists have theorized using nuclear power much like we do in submarines, but this also possesses an issue. There are two popular forms of nuclear power, the first being a nuclear fusion reactor and the other being a nuclear fission reactor. Powering these mechs with nuclear power would be difficult, as modern day fusion reactors are about the size of a warehouse and would cause more problems than they are worth. Until we are able to shrink down the reactor, this is not a viable option. Next is the nuclear fission reactors, which are primarily seen on submarines and other wartime vessels. These reactors, though efficient, can be very unsafe for pilot and civilians alike. Say a Kaiju is able to damage the reactor while in combat, the danger of fallout would be very real and could potentially cause more damage than the Kaiju would have.

The last and most attractive option is having the mechs plugged in. Mechs would be connected to a long power cord that is connected to an energy source. The mechs would then be able to move around more freely without the fear of power depletion. They would only be limited by the length of the cords. One of the potential drawbacks of this are the power source itself. Many believe the mechs would still need to be hooked up to a nuclear reactor of some sort in order to gain enough power. This could put them in close proximity to the same reactors that we are hoping to avoid.

3. Pilot

The issue of piloting the mech is another problem we face. The idea that a 100ft tall robot could be piloted by just one individual is not entirely out of the question, but it might prove too difficult in practice. Even something as advanced as a tank requires a minimum of three personnel to operate it. The other option for a potential pilot is for an artificial intelligence (AI) to be used instead of human pilots. While an AI could potentially mitigate the mech's complex operating systems easier than a human pilot, it can have problems in sensing and contextual decision making. This could lead to issues with the AI navigating the environment as well as applying appropriate force depending on the situation. In short, the mech needs a human touch. A good coupling of a powerful AI and skilled pilot could be the best answer, however, we still need to develop such a capable AI.

4. Size

In order for these mechs to be effective against the Kaiju, they need to at least match them in size, but this large size could cause more problems than solutions. The mechs would face issues with balance and speed. Another issue facing such large creations is the output of power. As stated by the Square Cube Relationship, if you make something twice as tall, wide, or thick, it will become eight times heavier but only four times stronger. This is something the Kaiju face as well, but their natural size has allowed their bodies more maneuverability. This means that even if a mech was equal size with a Kaiju, it is unlikely to overpower such a monster.

5. Transportation

Let's say that we are able to build such powerful weapons that could bring even the fiercest Kaiju to heel, how would we transport them? Part of what makes our military so powerful is the ability to transport thousands of troops, weapons, and vehicles in a matter of hours to anywhere in the world. This is something that, due to the randomness and uncertainty of a Kaiju attack, we must have the capability to do. While a mech could simply walk to the location, this would run its battery to an unnecessary extent and potentially cause issues in battle.

Another thought is being able to transport the mech via helicopters so that they could be dropped into battle. This is a horrible idea. Not only is it a logistical nightmare for air traffic controllers and flight crew personnel, but it is also impossible. Our aircraft can lift some heavy things, but not a giant robot. The last option and most practical is having at least one mech per major area that can be on hand should a Kaiju touch down and attack. This of course would be very expensive to maintain but given the impending doom of a Kaiju attack, it may be the best option.

6. Exo Suit

While we are a long time away from building any mechs, we are much closer to creating exo-suits. Exo-suits have a wide range of appearance and capability, although they are all smaller than what would be considered a mech. An exo-suit is designed to be worn by an individual and help improve their strength and durability. These suits are primarily created with military and construction applications in mind. Although they won't give a soldier any super powers like you see in movies, they will allow them to lift heavier weights and carry more combat gear then previously possible. These suits are still a few years away, but they are much closer to reality then the mechs we need to fight the Kaiju. Exo-suits will never put us on equal footing with the Kaiju, but they will help keep our troops alive. The possibility of a soldier being able to lift debris in order to rescue civilians is reason enough to pursue this application.

7. Future Necessity

While the usefulness of mechs is unquestionable, the issues we face in creating them are leading us to continue to use our conventional warfare techniques. Scientists would need to advance robotics, artificial intelligence, and nuclear science for us to have a mech similar to anything we have seen in the movies. We are sadly still years away from such strides, but we are hard at work. We are currently creating mechs that move like tanks and possess similar firepower. We may still be far away from 100ft tall robots, but maybe one day we'll get there.

USS KRAKEN

Branson, Missouri

Mrs. Brandt just finished recounting the story of how she and Michael met before taking their children to bed. Michael, a former Navy corpsman, was an enlisted crew member on board the USS Kraken. The Kraken is the submarine that saved the remaining lifeboats from the Kaiju in Glacier Bay, Alaska.

I think what I remember most is how tired I was. Life on a submarine can be hectic. You are constantly moving from one task to another. Each one is of the upmost importance. This made sleep the most valuable commodity on board. Hell, one time, I was awake for 36 hours straight without so much as a nap before I was finally able to sleep. I only got about an hour of sleep before something else broke and I had to be awake for another 36 hours. That was just how it was on board. My official job was a machinist mate for the weapons, but everyone wore a lot of hats. By the end of your first few weeks at sea, you would be an amateur firefighter, navigator, and electrician. That's just after the first few weeks too. You should see the skills that some guys come away with after a six-month deployment.

We had already spent a significant time at sea before the issue with the Kaiju. It was going on month five of the most boring deployment I had ever been on. The Kraken was what's called a fast attack submarine, which means that we hit our target hard and fast during wartime situations. That meant we were typically pretty active during our deployment. During this deployment though, we were there in a support role. We were at the Alaskan Coast. The only thing that we had any chance of going up against was the Russians, which wasn't going to happen anytime soon. So naturally, when we first got the call from the Coast Guard, we were giddy with excitement.

How far were you from Glacier Bay?

We were about two hours out, so not very far but still far enough that we weren't sure if there would be anyone left by time we showed up. The Coast Guard had received the distress call early that morning, but the fact that it was a Kaiju meant they were unequipped to deal with it. I think they did some flybys on their helicopters but weren't able to load any passengers to safety. The primary objective was to eliminate the Kaiju, or at the very least, get it far enough away so that we could get the survivors to safety. Of course that presented another problem on its own. How could we fire at something that was so close to civilians?

What did you do?

Once we got within the area, we deployed what's called sonar decoys.

When released, this device emitted a sonar signal that created false targets. We use it in wartime to trick hostile torpedoes into hitting the decoy and missing us altogether. Our hope was that we would release a few of these things and it would be enough to grab the Kaiju's attention, and as it turned out, we were right. We set a few decoys in the water outside of Glacier Bay and then we waited, and waited...and waited. Finally, after nearly a half-hour of waiting, a large blip began to appear on the sonar. The beast had heard us calling, and he was coming for us.

Were you next to the decoys during all of this?

Negative. We had dropped off the decoys and then circled back so that we had a good distance between us and them. Kaiju don't move like a submarine, they are typically much more maneuverable. We wanted to be as far away from this thing as possible while still maintaining an effective range for our torpedoes. Should we fire on the Kaiju and miss, then one of two things would happen. Scenario A was that the torpedoes scare the thing enough that it retreats back to the bottom of the ocean. Scenario B was that we piss it off and it starts coming right towards us. In the event of Scenario B, we would need to move fast so that we could re-position the sub in order to attempt a re-fire. Any false move on our part and we join the cruise ship at the bottom of the ocean.

By the time he came out of Glacier Bay, we were fully submerged and waiting for him to come to us. We had the torpedoes loaded up and ready to go and we're just waiting for the fire call. It was so quiet on board, I swear I could hear my own stomach digesting my lunch from earlier. Everyone on board was hanging on the captain's orders, just waiting to unleash hell on this thing. We let it get a little closer before finally, the captain gave the order and the Kraken fired two torpedoes right at the monster's head, and then we waited again. Waited and listened for those sweet words of a direct hit. It was different firing at this thing than it would be if we were attacking another submarine. Due to the fact that this thing was more maneuverable, we had to fire at the area surrounding the creature. The hope was that if one torpedo didn't hit him then at the very least, it would block him from escaping while the other one hit nearby. It sounds like that's exactly what happened too. Upon firing the torpedoes, the Kaiju realized something was up and began swimming towards us. The first torpedo was a miss but the second was a near direct hit. We began to celebrate but only for a few seconds as the sonar technician quickly went into a panic, notifying the whole ship this thing was still coming right at us. It appeared that Scenario B was in full effect. Not only was this thing pissed off but now we knew that it could take a blast from a torpedo almost head-on. This meant that whatever we hit it with next had to be as direct a shot as you could get. Without hesitation, we were already loading up the next torpedoes. The captain began to bark out orders for repositioning the sub. There was no way we were going to outrun this thing, but if we can get a better angle then hopefully we might be able to get a direct shot.

The feeling on board was tense to say the least. I remember thinking that I would never complain about boredom on a deployment again. We loaded the new torpedoes into place. This thing was barreling at us, and although we couldn't see it, the sound of the sonar beeping was enough to keep our buttholes clenched. As the creature got closer, the beeps increased in rhythm, adding to the already tense setting. Everyone was starting to yell for us to fire at the creature, but the captain waited to give the order. He waited until the creature was well within range before he made the call.

"Fire!" he said, and no words have ever been sweeter. We launched both torpedoes at the creature. Both were direct hits, as we were close enough to the impact that we could feel it within the submarine. Although there was no physical damage to the sub, the impact from those two torpedoes were enough to knock some of our equipment out of whack and send most of us on our asses, thoroughly unclenching our asses in the process. Long story short, the cruise ship passengers weren't the only ones that needed help at the end of the day.

[He smiles as he takes a sip from his beer.]

That was my last deployment for the rest of my time in the service. I got out of the Navy, came back home, and started going to school. That's where I met Meredith and the rest, as they say, is history. There's not a day that goes by that I don't think about that Kaiju, and how differently everything could've gone. I wish that I could sit here with a straight face and say that we beat this thing because of our skill and professionalism, but the truth is that we were lucky, very lucky. You could replay that whole scenario back another 100 times and I don't think we come out on top any of those times. I can't imagine what it must be like on the submarines now, with all the anti-Kaiju technology I keep hearing about in the news. It's amazing to me that we not only live in a world full of monsters, but that we are fighting them too. The fact that my kids are going to grow up in a world where a giant sea monster attack is just another Tuesday is still mind-blowing to me. I can't wait to see what the future holds, or what role the KRSD will play in it.

HELLBAT

Hill AFB, Utah

I am sitting in Lieutenant Colonel Ogden's office. Colonel Ogden is not what you typically think of when you imagine a squadron commander and decorated war hero. He sits with his feet kicked up on his desk and a 5 o'clock shadow on his face. I look around the room to see all of the typical awards, medals, and degrees that are seen in a squadron commander's office. It would all seem fairly normal if it weren't for the giant glass case hanging behind the colonel's chair. Within the glass case, titled "Hellbat Wing," is a giant bone fragment with a picture right below it showing a large bat-like creature dead on the ground with five men in flight suits standing around it, holding its face up and smiling while giving

the thumbs up. It reminds me of the old historical photos of big game hunters.

It was 1300Z when we got the call about the situation at the California coast. At the time, our meteorologists weren't sure if they were tracking a normal storm or if this was a potential Kaiju. Over the years, the military has made it a point to pay close attention to unexpected weather phenomena around the country. The storm was one such phenomena. Usually, the Navy would deal with these things, but they weren't seeing anything on their scopes, just fog, but no movement in the water. We started to think that this was just a freak storm when, at 1400, we received another call from the Navy. Something had flown past one of their destroyers. It was too big to be an aircraft and it wasn't showing up on their radar. It wasn't until they turned on the heat signatures that they saw the shape of a large winged creature in the fog. I guess by that point, it was already out of range, or it was just too close to the coast and they didn't want to risk hitting any civilians. Either way, we got the call and scrambled the Jets to intercept this thing.

To say that we were excited would be an understatement. We have been running combat simulations on these things for years now and many of us had never even seen one up close. The Navy, on the other hand, had seen hundreds of them and didn't mind rubbing it in from time to time. It was a healthy competition, one that motivated us to meet the threat head-on. We launched eight A10's from Hill Air Force Base under the callsign of WARTHOG31. It took us almost an hour to fly to Northern California. We were talking shit the entire way, betting who was going to get the kill and the glory. Of course, that all changed when we finally got to the coast and saw some of the damage that had already been done. The area was still fairly foggy, but you could see enough to know that this thing was dangerous. Buildings were knocked over and on fire. Emergency responders in the National Guard were on the ground trying to help as many people as they could. It was complete chaos. At that moment, the joking stopped and we were all business.

The fog was hard to see through, so we turned on our thermals and began patrolling the area. It wasn't long before we saw the damn thing helping itself to the highway snack. It was attacking civilians on the road, taking them out of their vehicles and swallowing them whole. As soon as we got it in our sights, command gave us the go ahead to fire and we lit that son of a bitch up. The A10 isn't the most maneuverable plane, but she kicks like a mule. If the mule had machine guns and ran on jet fuel and freedom. We were shooting to kill but only winged the creature. That was fine by us, though. We pissed it off enough that it left the civilians alone and began flying towards us. It may have been a monster, but we owned those skies, that was our domain, and we were going to make sure that he knew it. We kept our standard formation and did our best to keep our distance from this thing. Most people, when they think of dogfighting, they think back to the World War Two days where planes had to get up close and personal in order to be effective. In modern warfare, we are just as lethal at a distance, but lucky for us, the A10 is a diverse lady and is comfortable in any situation.

So, everything went off without a hitch?

Not exactly. I guess you could say that we started to get a little too comfortable, a little too cocky. We were hitting this thing with everything we had and it couldn't seem to keep up. I would attack it from one side and my wingman would attack it from another. It was visibly hurt and probably wouldn't be flying around for much longer. This motivated one of our wingmen, who shall remain nameless, to try and claim all the glory for himself. He got a little overzealous and broke formation. He then swooped around the air, cutting the bat off and now flying towards it head-on. We of course climbed so that we wouldn't get caught in the crossfire. Just when it looked like the killing blow was about to be delivered, the bat stopped itself mid-flight, brought its wings back, and then flapped them towards WARTHOG34. Its wings came together so hard, I swear it sounded like a rocket. All of a sudden, you saw WARTHOG34's left wing split in half and it began to fall. Luckily, 34's pilot activated his chute just in time, a few seconds more and the plane would've been spinning out of control too much for it to matter. This thing was somehow able to muster up enough strength to break the sound barrier in the WARTHOG34's direction. I don't know the technical term for it, but he essentially had the ability to shoot us with sound. This little display of power was enough motivation for us to finish him off. We got back in formation and executed our plan without any further issue. We fired at the thing with everything we had and then we kept on firing until he did a nosedive to the ground below.

And WARTHOG34?

He broke both of his legs and a couple of ribs, but given the circumstances, he was okay. That was the first time the U.S. military had ever dealt with an Aero Class Kaiju. All things considered, we did pretty well with it. Unfortunately, this thing was just a taste of things to come. Over the years, the U.S. alone has faced a total of six Aero Kaiju, more than any other country. Our Air Force is impressive, but it's not invincible. To date, our battle with the bat monster is the only air-to-air combat with a Kaiju where all aircrew lived. Some people will be quick to blame the quality of pilot our military is producing, but I don't agree with that, not one bit. No, I think these things are getting smarter, faster, stronger. I think they are evolving and that it'll be only a matter of time before they leave us in the dust.

ON THE ATTACK

FIGHTING THE KAIJU MENACE

Much of this book focuses on the Kaiju, their behaviors and motivations, but this section focuses on their weaknesses. More importantly, this section will tell you, as a civilian, how to kill the Kaiju, or at the very least, severely wound them.

As a warning, if you are a civilian, your primary goal against the Kaiju should always be escape. Regardless of how many action movies you have seen, how big your gun collection is, or what sweet karate moves you think you know, you are not trained, and more often than not, you do not possess sufficient firepower to deal with such a large creature. With all that said, you may find yourself in a situation where running and hiding is not an option. It is in that situation that this section could be useful.

CIVILIANS VS. KAIJU

Kaiju are essentially animals, very large and dangerous animals, but their behavior is essentially that of an animal. What does this mean for you? This means that in some ways, a Kaiju can be predictable.

When a Kaiju makes landfall, it has one primary goal, which is to gather energy. For most Kaiju, this is done by eating, and by using their impressive senses, most Kaiju will go straight for the most populated areas—the areas with the most food.

WEAKNESSES

Kaiju are like any other living creature. They possess organs and vital body parts that when attacked, could cause them serious damage or even death. An example of these are the heart, lungs, brain, or eyes. The challenges one faces when attacking these vital organs comes from the creature's impressive size, durability, or the lack of firepower at one's disposal. These creatures typically have very thick skin protecting the rest of their vital organs. A Kaiju's eyes are considered the most vulnerable point of attack on their body. This will blind the Kaiju and either let you escape or make it vulnerable for other attacks. The mouth is also a good area to fire at, as you could potentially damage its inner organs through that route. This can also be tricky, however, as a creature usually has the same thickness inside its body as it does the outside. If you are unable to damage these vital parts, then your next best option is to damage it by using other means. In the past, Kaiju have been killed using fire, electricity, or even extreme cold. While not many civilians have giant tasers lying around, a little gasoline and a well-placed trap can go a long way.

RULES TO FOLLOW: Follow these rules, in no particular order, when facing the Kaiju threat head-on.

1. LAWS & REGULATIONS

Ultimately, the firearms and other weapons you will have at your disposal will depend on the area you live in. Certain areas (cities, states, countries) do not allow their civilians to carry military-grade firearms, or firearms in general for that matter. When the Kaiju begin to attack, it is very important to not get in the way of the military or the first responders. A Kaiju attack, of any sort, is pure chaos in the best of scenarios. You, as an untrained civilian, are not going to be able to have some vast understanding that the other first responders do not. These are trained professionals that deal with emergency situations every day. Just because you know how to fire a gun or are an experienced hunter **DOES NOT** mean you know anything about dealing with a Kaiju. Too often, a local militia or a few gun aficionados will arrive on scene to a Kaiju attack with the intention to help. They will fire upon the monster with every piece of artillery at their disposal, paying little attention to the first responders or civilians in the crossfire. Once the dust clears, and all their firepower is expended, the militia is now faced with a few more hurt civilians and a severely pissed off Kaiju (the worst kind of Kaiju). The best thing to do if you are armed during a Kaiju attack is to protect yourself/those around you and ask the first responders how you can assist them. This will help create some much needed order during a Kaiju attack.

2. TRAIN

No matter the arsenal at your disposal, you need to be familiar with your weapons. Whether it is a pocket knife (don't attack a Kaiju with a pocket knife) or a cannon (where did you get a cannon?), it is important to train as much as possible with these weapons. Someone not properly trained in the use of firearms can be as much a danger as the Kaiju. With your weapon of choice, you must be familiar with its handling and maintenance. Be familiar with assembly and disassembly of all available firearms as well as safe troubleshooting techniques. It is highly advised that you get properly trained by a weapons specialist if you have access to one. Training with these weapons will not only give you more confidence but also make you better equipped to deal with the Kaiju.

3. HONE YOUR BODY

While you should never attempt hand-to-hand combat with a Kaiju (they will eat you), your body is your greatest weapon against the Kaiju menace. Kaiju are this world's alpha predator. In many ways, they are a perfect killing machine. When they attack a city full of people, sometimes the only thing that keeps you alive over others is your ability to outrun those around you. Your body must always be cared for in this dangerous and uncontrollable world. A Kaiju attack could happen without warning, and when it does, you must be ready for survival. This could mean more than simply having to outrun those around you. Bullets will run out eventually, so you may need to be prepared—both physically and mentally—for surviving out in the open for a few days. Surviving these conditions will be much easier if you are in good physical condition.

4. TEAMWORK

When facing the Kaiju threat, there is definite strength in numbers. These monsters are bigger, faster, and stronger than any human on the planet. As a team or unit, you can combine your efforts to lure and trap these monsters. These creatures are too big and too powerful for one civilian to do much damage, however a small group, trained and coordinated, could be enough to bring even the fiercest of monsters down. Even the most well-trained individual will be food if they attempt to attack a Kaiju alone.

5. HAVE AN ESCAPE

Should things take a turn for the worst, and they very easily can, it is important to always have an escape plan. It is highly unlikely that you will be able to eliminate a Kaiju with an all-out assault. Instead, you should hit it from the shadows, damaging it from a safe distance. Should you run out of weapons or supplies, you always want to be able to sneak back into the safety of a shelter, whether it is a secured or improvised one. Never leave yourself out in the open for an attack.

6. BE THE HUNTER, NOT THE HUNTED

Everything we know about the Kaiju indicates that they have intelligence no greater than an animal, meaning they're fueled by only their basic instincts. This can be used to your advantage when combating the Kaiju, who will act on instinct alone. You are able to plan, organize, and direct the Kaiju to your benefit. Your deadliest weapon is your mind, and it should be used every chance you get.

7. COMMUNICATION

The best teams are successful in large part thanks to their communication skills, and this is no different when hunting Kaiju. Coordination amongst team members could be all that keeps you alive in a Kaiju attack. Make sure that you have the ability to talk to each other either using radios or other devices, such as lights or even hand signals. This will help you to coordinate from a safe distance, surround the Kaiju, and unleash your arsenal upon it.

8. SAFETY FIRST

The importance of safety cannot be stressed enough in this section. The proper use of your equipment is the best way to keep you and your loved ones safe. Too many people have weapons and gear that they are not familiar with nor properly trained in. This often makes them more of a danger to the group than the actual Kaiju. Safety also needs to be a priority when planning and executing any operation. Never take unnecessary risks that could put you or members of your team in danger. It won't make you a hero; it will make you Kaiju food.

9. HAZARDOUS MATERIALS

Some groups rely more on traps over actual artillery. This is fine, and in many cases, will work out well for the group. However, whether it is incendiary devices or dangerous chemicals, it is important to exercise extreme caution with such materials. Like any firearm, the misuse of these weapons could prove fatal for the whole group. Past survivalist groups have been on the receiving end of their own traps. They will acquire explosives or poisonous material, only to mishandle it and have it quite literally blow up in their faces. Don't be these people. Exercise extreme caution with these items.

10. KNOW THE AREA

If you find yourself in unfamiliar territory, it is better to find shelter and then explore. Your familiarity with your surroundings could help you to better plan for a Kaiju attack. Knowing what areas are safe or hard to reach can be a great benefit should you lose your primary shelter. Knowing the area can also help you with warning signs of a potential Kaiju attack. Sometimes Kaiju movement isn't as obvious as a large footprint and pushed-over buildings, sometimes it can be something minor like pushed-up segments of earth or knocked-over tree limbs. Whatever the case, having an intimate familiarity with your surroundings will help keep you safe and the Kaiju confused.

11. WATCH FOR WARNING SIGNS

It may seem hard to believe, but Kaiju can disappear almost into thin air sometimes. One minute, they are terrorizing a city and the next, they are gone, with seemingly no explanation. Whatever the reason for their retreat, this is not the time to let your guard down. Continue to watch for signs of Kaiju movement, such as tremors or changes in the weather. If possible, it is important to have access to the emergency broadcast stations and listen to them when you know a Kaiju is in the area. Remember, they can always reappear just as fast as they disappeared.

WEAPONS/GEAR

When going after or defending yourself from a Kaiju, it is important to have the right gear. Planning for a Kaiju attack can be tricky, since no two Kaiju seem to be the same and finding a weakness can be a process of trial and error. It is not as simple as grabbing the biggest gun you have, forming a posse, and going Kaiju hunting. Attacking these creatures is something that requires the utmost planning and precision. The first and best way to do that is by ensuring you have the proper weapons available in order to fight the Kaiju menace. This section will detail different types of weapons used in the slaying of Kaiju. While not all of these are readily available to civilians, it is still important to have a basic understanding of these weapons and their usefulness in the field.

FIREARMS

When dealing with the Kaiju threat, no weapon will be more important than the firearms in your arsenal. The type of firearm you choose will ultimately decide how you deal with the Kaiju threat, as well as your role in the team of survivors. There are many different types of firearms, all for different scenarios and threats. Whatever is chosen, you must make sure that you are trained in how to properly handle and care for that weapon. Below is a description of just some of the potential firearms at your disposal.

1. HANDGUN

A handgun is a firearm that is designed to be handheld and fired easily using one or both hands. We see these types of guns all over movies and television. At this point, we should be very familiar with them as a society. A handgun comes in many different types, such as the revolver, pistols, or even pepperboxes, however the purpose remains the same. These firearms are meant to be small and easy to carry, and they are ideal for self-defense. The range and power of each handgun depends on its type, as well as any modifications made to it.

While useful for self-defense, a handgun is not the most useful firearm in the event of a Kaiju attack. These firearms will normally do little more than agitate a Kaiju, unless it's a well-placed shot to its eyes or face and even then, it is unlikely to seriously wound it. While the handgun is not particularly useful against the Kaiju threat, its use as a tool for self-defense is invaluable. The handgun also has the indispensable feature of using the same ammunition with other firearms such as a carbine. This makes the handgun extra useful as it can eliminate the amount of ammunition you need to carry on your person.

2. CARBINES

A carbine is a unique firearm that possesses a longer barrel than a handgun—usually up to 20 inches in length—but still shorter than a rifle. Many carbines are shortened versions of rifles that shoot the same ammunition. These firearms are very diverse in that they are capable of firing different rifle or pistol ammunition depending on the type of carbine. These firearms are lightweight and easy to handle. The major drawback the carbine faces is its inferior long-range accuracy when compared to that of a rifle. While the carbine doesn't have the range or accuracy of a rifle, they have more controllability than a pistol. This can make them better for hitting Kaiju at range then a handgun, however the damage would not be much better.

3. RIFLES

A rifle is typically a gun fired from the shoulder that is used to shoot for both distance and accuracy. Traditionally, rifles were used for hunting and were only capable of firing a single shot for each trigger pull, however, modern rifles are capable of firing multiple bullets with one pull of the trigger. A rifle is a good weapon to have on hand for a Kaiju attack, thanks to its range and accuracy, allowing the shooter to be a relatively safe distance away while attacking the Kaiju. Additionally, thanks to the many attachments associated with the rifle, it is capable of being upgraded to a very diverse killing machine.

There are many different variations of a standard rifle, so many in fact that we will not go into them. It is important to do your research and find which rifle best suits your needs.

There are typically two different types. The first is an automatic rifle (also known as an assault rifle), which was first introduced in WWII. Although they were slowly embraced, they are now the premiere weapon of choice for most of the world's military forces. What separates assault rifles from conventional rifles is the fact that they are capable of selective fire. This means that with each pull of the trigger, automatic rifles can rotate between firing one shot at a time to firing multiple shots. This of course can be very devastating and dangerous to your target. Due to the danger they present, most high-powered assault rifles are not available to anyone other than military or law enforcement. When discussing the assault rifle, we are typically speaking of weapons such as the AK-47, StG 44, and the M16.

A semiautomatic rifle, much like an automatic rifle, is fed ammunition using a cartridge. This rifle however is much more conventional in that it will only fire one shot for each trigger pull. While it can still be very dangerous, this rifle is considered the safer of the two types due to the control it typically allows its user to have.

Any firearm will give you some kickback when you fire it. This kickback is sometimes so powerful it could knock down a full-grown man. Such a loss of control can cause the shooter to fire randomly, possibly hurting those nearby. This danger is present when dealing with an assault rifle, as the constant fire will knock even the strongest of humans back. As long as you have a proper stance, you should be okay, however, most targets, especially Kaiju, won't just sit there and wait for you to shoot them.

4. SNIPER RIFLE

A sniper rifle is the best rifle to use in terms of both range and accuracy. While the effective range of these rifles depends on the model being used, long-range models are able to hit targets over a mile and a half away with precision. This would allow for the shooter to be a safe distance from the Kaiju while firing. The drawback to sniper rifles are the fact that they are long and cumbersome, making them difficult to transport. This could be an issue should the shooter need to expeditiously evacuate the area. The other main drawback to using a sniper rifle is the operator error itself. There is a lot more to effectively firing a gun than just looking down a scope and shooting. This is even more true when firing a sniper rifle. These weapons are capable of firing great distances with pinpoint accuracy if they are fired by a skilled marksman. The accuracy of each shot is determined by many uncontrollable factors. Each shooter should be familiar with their surroundings, the wind speed and direction, as well as proper handling of their rifle. Once an individual is skilled with such a weapon, they are a force to be reckoned with by man and Kaiju alike.

5. SHOTGUNS

A shotgun, much like a rifle, is a firearm that is meant to be fired from the shoulder. This firearm fires two types of ammunition, either a shot or a slug. A slug is much like your typical bullet, just slightly bigger. It is meant to fire at a specific target. A shot, however, is a slug filled with tiny balls of ammunition that when fired, will spray over a specific area as opposed to just one target. Regardless of the ammunition used, the primary use of a shotgun is for firing at a target at close-range. These firearms will do immense amounts of damage to a target. While they are nightmares at close-range, a shotgun is not recommended against a Kaiju. Most shotguns lack range, and even if they do hit a target far away, they are far less likely to do as much damage as a rifle. The only time you could use such a weapon effectively against a Kaiju is at close-range, but unless you are shooting it in the eyes or face, being close to a Kaiju will almost certainly mean your demise.

6. SUBMACHINE GUN (SMG)

This fully automatic carbine was developed in WWI and is designed to fire pistol cartridges. Much like the shotgun, these weapons are effective at close to mid-range, but fall short to the range and accuracy of a rifle. This isn't to say that they are completely useless however, as SMG ammo can be mixed with that of pistols and other carbines, which can be useful if you do not want to travel with a variety of ammunition. The SMG is capable of penetrating helmets and body armor and is still used by military and police forces today for close quarters combat (CQB). While they can prove useful for personal defense, these weapons lack the range to be considered an effective Kaiju weapon.

7. HEAVY MACHINE GUN (HMG)

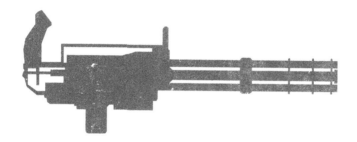

When referring to the heavy machine gun, people are either refer-ring to the pre-WWII HMG, which was classified as heavy due to its weight, or they are referring to the post-WWII firearms that are clas-sified as such due to their large-caliber rounds. For this book, we will be referring to the post-WWII HMG.

The modern-day HMG is a large-caliber machine gun that is capable of firing ammunition (typically .50 or 12.7 mm) capable of penetrating vehicles, buildings, or even aircraft. These weapons are highly effective in the field and can have considerable range. The only downside is their weight, with the medium models weighing over 30 pounds and the large models being so heavy that they need to be mounted to a vehicle. The HMG, when positioned correctly, can be very useful in taking the fight to the Kaiju. Its impressive range and damage capabilities make this a dream for would-be Kaiju slay-ers. To avoid any issues with its weight, it is recommended that you mount the HMG to a vehicle such as a truck and use it to attack from range while remaining mobile.

8. ROCKET LAUNCHER

It is very unlikely that a civilian would have a weapon such as a rocket launcher in their arsenal, just like it is unlikely they would have an HMG, assault rifles, or grenades, however, stranger things have happened. As improbable as it may seem for you to acquire these weapons, the fact remains that if you come across them in the field, you need to be familiar with them. These weapons have been seen in every action movie and video game since the 1980s, so while it is assumed everyone knows what they are, we will still discuss the basics.

A rocket launcher, or bazooka for some, is a projectile-based weapon capable of firing rockets, grenades, warheads, and other types of ammunition. It was primarily used by ground troops in WWII for eliminating tanks. This weapon is relatively easy to handle, weighing up to 20 pounds depending on the model. While the destructive power of these weapons depends on the model and ammunition being used, the results, even with the worst version, can be devastating to a target.

If you should have access to such an artillery, it is recommended that you train with it and practice the utmost safety. One wrong move and the rocket launcher could eliminate you and everyone around you. Capable of firing up to 350 yards, the rocket launcher is useful in any situation, allowing for its users to attack from far away or up close (though not recommended). While you could easily hop in the back of a pickup truck with a loaded bazooka to go kill some Kaiju, the moving vehicle may prove too unsafe. It is recommended that you find a strategic location where you are able to get proper footing and fire from there. Much like the shotgun and other firearms, the rocket launcher can have heavy kickback, knocking the user down in the process.

For this weapon, you want to pick your shots carefully and calmly. If you have multiple ammunition, then it is recommended to have a two-person team for firing the rocket. This will allow one person to fire while the other loads a new round into the cannon. If your group is able to corner or lure a Kaiju into an area where it is surrounded, then this weapon would prove very useful. It may not kill the Kaiju, but it should seriously maim or injure it.

9. FLAMETHROWER

A flamethrower is a mechanical device used to shoot a long, controlled stream of fire. These weapons can trace their origins all the way to ancient Greece and have shown themselves useful in some of the world's bloodiest conflicts. The military-grade flamethrower uses flammable liquid that burns the target or area on contact. Flamethrowers are also used in the civilian world for agriculture or other land management tasks. These flamethrowers typically use high-pressure propane and natural gas. Many believe this to be a safer alternative to the dangerous liquid used in the military.

As noted several times in this text, Kaiju have shown themselves vulnerable to fire in the past. On paper, this makes the flamethrower an optimal weapon for fighting the Kaiju, but in practice, using a flamethrower can be very difficult and dangerous. Flamethrowers can be very heavy, which will limit your mobility. It is for this reason that you should instead try to mount the flamethrower onto a vehicle or at least have the operator strapped into a vehicle. This way, mobility will not impede the war effort.

The next issue is time. Flamethrowers burn fuel very quickly, resulting in only a few seconds of actual fire. This means whoever is shooting the flames must be precise and careful with their shots.

The most glaring danger associated with a flamethrower is how vulnerable it makes the operator and those around them. In war, flamethrower operators were singled out by snipers. If one was able to hit or damage the chemical flamethrower's tank, then it would cause an explosion severe enough to kill the operator and those within close proximity. This is no different when dealing with Kaiju, who are capable of much more than a sniper. If a Kaiju were to damage the flamethrower tanks, it could put the rest of the group at risk. This needs to be a calculated risk if your group should decide to use flamethrowers. Unless you have a team of capable flamethrower operators, then your best bet might be to lure the Kaiju to a flammable area and use the flamethrower to light it up. While their range is not as impressive as firearms, they are still able to fire from up to 50 yards away. Regardless of if you use a flamethrower or not, fire is an undeniably useful weapon against the Kaiju.

10. GRENADES

Grenades can be very useful when dealing with the Kaiju threat. Whether it is to damage or distract the monsters, these small bombs should be carried on your person at all times, if possible. Grenades are small projectiles that are thrown at a target and detonate either on impact or after a short delay. Not all grenades have incendiary capabilities, once detonated. Some grenades will expel chemicals, tear gas, or flash bangs that can stun the target. This variety makes grenades a must-have on the battlefield.

Of course there are dangers, the first one being operator error. Grenades are designed to be thrown from a distance, however, people have been killed in the field simply by mishandling or even under throwing the grenade. Another issue is range, which depends largely on the individual throwing the grenade. There are cannons capable of firing grenades, but these are usually military weapons that aren't available to civilians. Additionally, the use of such a weapon would require the operator to be familiar with figuring the range of a target. Should the range be too little or too great then it could be wasted.

Figuring range would prove more difficult as well due to the fact that Kaiju rarely stay still.

11. BLADES/BLUDGEONS

Blades and bludgeons, the two most basic weapons that mankind has used on the battlefield since the dawn of time. Unfortunately for us, these two types of weapons will have little success against the Kaiju. While both can be useful in self-defense, it is not suggested to face a rampaging 50 feet tall beast with a sword. You may cut it, but it's unlikely you'll seriously hurt, let alone kill, it. Only the smallest of Kaiju would be affected by an attack from a handheld blade or bludgeon, and even then, it may only anger it. Blades such as knives are always good to have on hand for protection from people and animals alike, as well as aiding in survival tasks. A bludgeon such as a hammer has the same level of use. These two types of weapons, while not useful against Kaiju, should still be a part of any survivalist's gear.

12. CHEMICAL WARFARE

With the birth of modern warfare also came advances in science, which is clearest when discussing chemical warfare. Popularized in WWII, chemical warfare is the use of chemical agents on the battlefield to harm your enemy. These chemicals, once set off, can incapacitate the enemy, cause severe skin burns, or even choke them to death. While they are not used in today's "civilized" theater of war—at least, not by most of the world's governments—these weapons are still quite effective, with lesser agents such as tear gas being used by police forces all over the world. Against the Kaiju, such chemical weapons have had wild card effects to say the least. As stated before, no two Kaiju are the same, which means the weaknesses of one monster might not be shared by the rest. A blistering agent may severely effect one Kaiju, but do nothing to another. The point is that whenever using one of these chemical weapons against a Kaiju, you will have a random chance of success.

The good news is that Kaiju are still organisms and so far, we have not found any of them to be completely immune to *all* chemical agents. The bad news is that in the field, you may not have many options for which chemicals to use, if any. The important thing to remember is that when using such weapons, have the proper safety equipment such as gasmasks and skin protection. It is also important to handle these weapons carefully. Unless you are a well-equipped chemist, you are not qualified to handle such material, which means you should be as careful as humanly possible.

PERSONAL GEAR

Below is a list of gear each Kaiju-slayer should have on their person at all times. This gear can change depending on the terrain and situation, however it is always advised to have these main items on you while in the field.

- A primary firearm
  - Ammunition for primary firearm
  - Cleaning kit
  - Secondary weapon (firearm or other)
  - Ammunition for secondary weapon, if applicable
  - Knife (or blade of some sort)
  - Flashlight
  - Water-proof matches or lighter
  - Flares
  - Canteen
  - Water-purifying packets
  - Personal first aid kit
  - Daily rations
  - Socks
  - Eye protection
  - Bedroll/pad
  - Protective equipment (gloves, pads, helmet)
  - Gasmask or face protection of some sort

ADDITIONAL GEAR

If traveling in a group, it is encouraged to have additional pieces of gear carried amongst the group. This will allow for greater resources in the field, as well as coordination. Some of the extra gear carried should include but not be limited to:

- Additional ammunition
    - Explosive devices (detonators, incendiary, grenades)
    - Flares
    - Flare gun
    - Binoculars
    - Tools (crowbar, hammer, bolt cutters)
    - Toolkit (screws, wrenches, tape)
    - Additional medical supplies
    - Maps
    - Water
    - Compass
    - Batteries
    - Signaling mirror

STRATEGIES

Below are potential strategies that civilians have used in the field. Even though these strategies were for the most part well planned and executed, they were still met with casualties. This is to be expected when dealing with a creature as powerful as a Kaiju. It should also be noted that these strategies were primarily used against Category I and II Terra Class Kaiju. A Category III Kaiju is considered too big and too powerful for most of these tactics to prove effective. This is not to say that civilians have not been able to eliminate a Category III in the past, but only after the Kaiju was already damaged by military artillery. The tactics listed below assume they are being carried out by civilians with civilian artillery and little to no combat experience.

1. LURE AND DESTROY

Kaiju are simple creatures who seem to be motivated by consuming food or energy. This is a predictable behavior that can be exploited. If you have access to a large meat supply or livestock, then you can set it in an area of your choice. This area should have traps that if able, destroy the Kaiju once it gets close enough to the bait. If you are unable to destroy the monster, then your next best option is to seriously maim or damage it so that it cannot give chase. With any luck, it will succumb to its injuries over time. If you are able to trap a Kaiju, then it is highly encouraged that you eliminate it as soon as possible. While the temptation is there to trap and study such a specimen, as a civilian, it is likely that any tests conducted without proper gear or facilities would end in slaughter. Some useful traps that have worked in the past on smaller Kaiju are pits and snares. On the larger Category III and higher, such traps would be ineffective and those should instead be dealt with using incendiaries.

2. BARRICADE

When speaking of barricades, we are talking about walls, gates, or even large debris that can be used to stop or even corral the Kaiju's movement. Some rural towns and major cities have even begun constructing walls around themselves in order to keep their residents safe and the Kaiju out. While this can be useful against some Kaiju, it is not a permanent solution by any means, with most Kaiju having enough strength to penetrate even the toughest of structures. Because of this, the walls are usually manned by watchmen that can signal the residents when a Kaiju is inbound. These guards are usually armed with rifles and have heavy artillery placed at strategic points along the wall. This heavy artillery ranges from anything from a chain gun to a cannon.

Such barricades are only in a few areas around the world. As for the rest of the world, if you are aware of a Kaiju inbound to your location, you will have to do the best with what you have. This means getting organized and surrounding yourself with large moveable objects, such as trucks, buses, or even RVs. Once you have a perimeter set up, then enact the same strategies listed above. Arm the barricades, move those that can't fight to a secure location, and attempt to stop or redirect the Kaiju. With any luck, you will either kill it or discourage it enough to leave the area.

3. THE HIGH GROUND

The high ground is important in any type of combat, whether against people or Kaiju. The high ground could be a cliff, water tower, building, fire watch, or even a tree. The point is to be higher than or equal to the Kaiju in height, preferably higher. This area should be outfitted with enough supplies and ammunition to last a while. However, if you're dealing with a Kaiju capable of climbing, then you may only need the ammunition and a good escape plan. This position is ideal for someone with a high-range weapon like a sniper rifle. You will want to shoot your target in the vital parts of the body such as the eyes or face, and then be prepared to move from your position at a moment's notice should the Kaiju wise up to your location. Some snipers even go as far to booby trap their towers so that when a Kaiju does attack, it is met with further destruction.

4. RAM IT

While we will never match the Kaiju in strength or speed, we possess vehicles that come close. This method is not advised unless you are a skilled driver or have a particularly sturdy vehicle. In the past, survivors have used larger vehicles such as buses, RVs, construction equipment, or even garbage trucks to damage the Kaiju by ramming into them. Some even go a step further, outfitting their vehicles with all types of spikes or blades to hurt the Kaiju further.

Drivers skilled with construction vehicles, such as bulldozers, have been particularly effective against the Kaiju and are encouraged use them, if available. In urban areas, there have even been reports of train conductors using trains against the Kaiju by attempting to corner/trap them on the tracks and run into them.

These methods usually result in severe injuries or even death for the driver and crew, but have been shown to be effective against the Kaiju.

5. CONVOY ATTACK

This method requires the survivors to go on the offensive in the broadest sense. A convoy would consist of multiple vehicles armed with weapons and personnel that are familiar with how to use them. In this strategy, you are either searching for or meeting the Kaiju head-on in an attempt to catch it off guard and overwhelm it with your numbers and aggression. You will have to load up your well-armed posse in your most durable vehicles and travel in an orderly fashion towards the Kaiju. Once you come into contact with the beast, your occupants will begin to fire at the Kaiju. You could adopt this tactic as a way to lure the Kaiju into a trap of some sort by getting its attention and then retreating to a safe location while it follows.

This method as a whole is not highly recommended, as any stray bullet or poor driving could lead to disaster for your group without the Kaiju even touching you. It is very important that members of your group maintain an orderly fashion when engaging the Kaiju. If you do adopt this battle technique, then be sure to plan your formation ahead of time and not engage the target over unfamiliar terrain.

6. AIRBORNE ATTACK

Attacking a target from the air has many uses in conventional warfare. On paper, it would keep you safely out of harm's way while you attack from above. In practice against Kaiju, this has proven to be the furthest thing from the truth. Airpower is dominant in any theater of war, however the Kaiju tend to hit back when provoked. Whether they are slashing, biting, throwing, or grabbing at aircraft, the Kaiju have proven to be quite effective when it comes to dispatching aircraft that make the mistake of getting too close. For a military aircraft, this isn't as much of a concern as they can fire accurately from miles away. This is more of an issue, however, for civilian aircraft.

When speaking of civilian aircraft, we are talking about fixed-wing aircraft (with or without a propeller), helicopters, and even gliders. All of these are meant for air travel and not combat unless modified for such. If a group of survivors has an aircraft and a pilot to operate it, then their first priority should be using it as a means of escape from an approaching Kaiju. If escape is not an option, then the aircraft could be used to attack the Kaiju from above. It is not recommended to engage the Kaiju up close. You will want to stay well above the Kaiju and drop artillery on it from a safe distance.

While it is possible to attack a Kaiju using civilian aircraft, only helicopters or fixed-wing aircraft should be considered due to their speed and maneuverability. Something such as a hot air balloon would be of little help in a Kaiju attack, unless the Kaiju is capable of emitting an EMP of some sort.

Ultimately, though, these civilian aircraft should be saved for escape tools, bringing supplies from place to place, or acting as surveillance. It is not uncommon for a rampaging Kaiju to knock out communication for an entire area. In this case, having a plane capable of surveillance and tracking the Kaiju's movements would greatly benefit the survivors. A remote-operated drone is also very useful for this situation. A drone's use can further extend to bringing supplies and messages over short distances amongst other survivors.

Airborne attacks can be useful against ground targets, however, a Kaiju capable of flight is a fast, powerful creature capable of knocking over tanks and even small buildings with just a flap of its wings. They are a nightmare for the military to deal with, as their size and speed prevent most military aircraft from engaging them without being knocked out of the sky. Civilian aircraft should never engage an Aero

Class Kaiju in any way, shape, or form. These creatures are amongst the most dangerous of all Kaiju. They could knock your plane out of the sky before it even got close enough to fire a shot. Unless you are using your plane as a suicide tool, do not engage an airborne Kaiju.

7. BATTLE AT SEA

The strategy for a battle at sea is simple: there isn't one. For civilian vessels that aren't equipped with the most up-to-date anti-Kaiju weaponry, there isn't much of a chance for success. The sea is not a natural habitat for humans and if a Kaiju is there, then it is safe to assume they are well equipped for anything you or the ocean can throw at them. While there are things you can purchase to help defend your vessel from unwanted guests (pirates), there isn't anything capable of stopping a motivated Kaiju from destroying your ship. The best you can hope for is outrunning the Kaiju, which, given their usual size and speed, isn't likely.

BLOOD & OIL

Australian Coast

My next interview takes me to the Pennadine oil rig almost 200 miles off the eastern coast of Australia. The rig hasn't been active for a few years but serves as a reminder of one of the strangest series of Kaiju attacks in recent memory. Accompanying me via helicopter is Mr. Donald Williams, a former Pennadine worker who spent almost a year working on this rig. Mr. Williams witnessed the Kaiju attack firsthand. As we arrive to what is left of the rig, Mr. Williams begins to show me around. He walks me from one area to the next, explaining each area's purpose as we go. This continues until we get to a set of claw marks left within the pillars of the rig. This is where we decide to sit for our interview.

I worked on this rig, or rigs more like it, as a crane operator for the last 15 years. I didn't start out as a crane operator. No, I got that title the traditional way. I started as a roustabout at first, and then eventually made my way up to assistant crane operator before finally getting my full certifications.

What's a roustabout?

A roustabout is what you would call an entry-level position on an oil rig. They primarily help with loading and unloading the boats, but they do a lot of other things as well. You could call them a gopher of sorts. Some guys get their certifications done and then come on to the rig and start making the big bucks fairly quickly. That's not what I did, though. I came up through the ranks, pulled my weight and earned my position. It wasn't the fastest route, but I'm glad it's the one I took. On this rig, we would typically do 3 to 4-week long shifts. We were on week three of a four-week shift when the creature showed up.

I ask this a lot in my interviews, but did anything seem unusual during those days leading up to the creature's arrival?

In all honesty, I don't remember. Life on the rig is rough. We would work 12 to 14 hour days on average, with almost no downtime. That particular week, we had just gotten a new batch of roustabouts who were keeping me busy. So in all honesty, I don't remember many details leading up to the attack. I was too busy working and making sure everyone else was safe. It's very easy to screw something up and seriously get hurt in this profession. Hell, sometimes that happens even when things go perfectly. Every day on this rig brought with it new challenges that we had to overcome. I've read that storms can be a warning to a Kaiju's arrival, and while we most certainly had a few hairy weather days that month, nothing seemed out of the ordinary.

As we walk further, I begin to see more extensive damage throughout the rig. I see more claw marks on the walls, but most

chilling of all are the bent steel beams that are meant to withstand destructive tidal waves.

My crew and I had just finished securing all of our gear. We got word there was a storm inbound, so we called it a day. We had to make sure that everything is tied down and secure before we went to our cabins. The plan was then to wait out the storm and start work again as soon as it was over. It was around 6 PM by the time we finished getting everything secure and then we went below deck to wait out the storm. We weren't sure how long it would last, so my crew and I went to the cafeteria to get some grub. The storm wasn't particularly bad, but it didn't seem to be going away any time soon, so I released my crew. I went to my cabin to call my wife and get some shuteye. I figured that we would return to work early in the morning once the storm was done.

It was a little after midnight when I awoke to the rig's alarm system. This alarm could've meant a few different things, and some rigs even have multiple alarm systems, but ours didn't. As soon as we heard the alarm though, we were supposed to report to our superiors, take accountability for the crew, and go from there. As I was getting my jumpsuit and boots on, I was running through all of the possible situations in my head. I don't think I ever could've imagined what was actually causing the alarm, though. I hardly saw anyone as I made my way to the meeting point, which is unusual on a small rig of almost 200 people. What was even more usual, though, was the lack of information anyone had about the alarm going off. No one knew who triggered it or why it was going off. When I finally made my way to the meeting point, I came upon a group of almost 20 people yelling at the foreman, who was covered in mud and was blocking the door. It wasn't until I got closer that I realize that he wasn't covered in mud. He was drenched in blood. Everyone was yelling at him, wanting to know what was going on. The foreman looked like he was in shock. I told the guys to stop crowding him and give him some time to calm down before I asked him what was going on. He nervously took a few deep breaths and wiped the blood off of his face before he began to speak again. He talked about something coming on board and attacking him and a few of the other deckhands before he was able to pull the alarm and get away. He said that he didn't check for anyone behind him, he just ran back here and locked the door, and he said there was no way in hell he was going back out there.

Personally, I thought the guy had lost his marbles. He did have that blood on his face, though. That worried me. I was worried there was some sort of accident he saw and he just didn't know how to process it. At no point did I think it was a Kaiju or anything, but one thing was for certain, there were some people outside those doors that probably needed help. I organized a small search party consisting of myself and two others. The rest the guys were instructed to watch the blood-covered deckhand and take him to medical. I kept trying to get a hold of someone on the radio but wasn't having much luck. I hoped that once I got outside, I'd be able to get in touch with somebody. As we made our way up top, it became very clear that something was wrong. It looked like a struggle of some sort had taken place. There was blood splattered along the walls, destroyed equipment, and other machinery that would take weeks to replace. At first, I thought one of the machines had blown, until we looked at the door we just came from. It was covered in bloody handprints and claw marks. We were moving around pretty quietly at this point. The rain from the storm had stopped, but you could still hear the waves of the ocean swaying back and forth. As we looked around the area, we didn't see any signs of life. Even up at the guard shack.

The guard shack? There are guards on a rig?

Yes, depending where you are. Rigs are prone to all sorts of attacks, from pirates to wild environmentalists. It isn't uncommon for an oil rig to have a small security detail. When we walked up to the guard shack though, the door had been left open and there were no signs of any guards. We did see a few bullet shells on the ground, which raised a few red flags for us. At that point, we decided to head back and secure ourselves in the cabins below. We didn't know who or what was up here, but I wasn't about to take any chances. We started heading back when we heard something walking around. It sounded like something was scratching against the floor grates on deck. We snuck around the side so we could get a view of what was making the noise. That's when we first saw the Kaiju. It had its snakelike face deep into the remains of one of the guards who, aside from his uniform, was unrecognizable at that point. This thing was long and slender like a snake, but had these long arms and disproportionately short legs. I remember it was all sorts of colors, like a chameleon in a cartoon show. We took one look at that thing and started back towards the cabin. No way were we confronting anything like that.

Of course, as fate would have it, the walkie-talkie finally started to work, letting out a loud squelch, followed by one of my mates trying to get a hold of me and see what was going on up there. I turned it off as fast as I could, but it was too late. The creature had seen us, and it was locked in. Its head was bobbing all around as it began to hiss at us. The creature grew a hood on the sides of his head, like you the ones you see on a cobra or those spitting dinosaurs in the movies. We took off running and could hear him close behind. I turned on the radio again in an attempt to call someone on the emergency frequencies. Most rigs have at least one larger vessel floating nearby in case of emergencies. These vessels are constantly monitoring our frequencies and are there to help evacuate us or notify the Coast Guard. Myself and the two guys I was with all ended up running in completely different directions. I wish I could say it was some part of a strategy, but I think we were just scared as hell and trying to get away from the thing as fast as possible. Lucky for me it chose one of the other three and went for him. At this point, I was focused on notifying someone about what was going on above deck. As I ran around wildly, I saw the crane and thought it was probably my best place to hide out. At the very least, it would keep me hidden while I tried to get a hold of somebody. If all else failed, there was a flare gun inside the crane. I ran as fast as I could, ignoring the screams of the unfortunate soul that was just caught. I climbed into the crane, shut the door, and began yelling for help on the emergency frequency. The vessel below responded almost immediately, but they had a tough time understanding me. I was talking very fast. I'm sure I wasn't making a whole lot of sense.

Had they not heard the gunfire or anything earlier?

My guess is that the noise caused by the guards and this creature was masked by the storm. Either way though, they were on their way to help and I was staying put in the damn crane. I tried to switch frequencies to notify everyone in their cabins to stay down below, but I couldn't get a hold of anyone. Then, much to my horror, I began to see flashlights emerging from the cabin door. Turns out the boys got worried when they couldn't get a hold of us. They decided to come above deck and have a look. I didn't have eyes on the monster, but I knew it wouldn't be long before he heard them walking around. I wasn't about to lose any more men. I opened up the crane door, stuck my head out, and began to yell for them to run away. I must have looked like a madman waving my arms and screaming like that. I got their attention all right, but it didn't seem like they understood me. They kept yelling back, asking if I was alright. To make matters worse, they started walking towards me, that is, until they heard that hissing noise. They stopped dead in their tracks and shined their lights off the side of the rig where the Kaiju had coiled itself like a snake. Hanging from its mouth was one of the boys that came up with me. Unfortunately, it didn't look like he was able to outrun the beast. Once the lights were shining on the Kaiju, he dropped the body from his jaws. He launched from the side of the rig like a slithering demon. He wasted no time attacking these new victims. The men started to scream and the process repeated itself over again. I shut the door to the crane and started yelling at myself. It was my fault. I should've done more to stop them. That's all I could think about. I was having a panic attack right there in the crane. I needed to do something, but I didn't know what. That's when I got the idea to start up the crane. I figured I could at least distract the damn thing with moving around. At best, I was hoping I would be able to do some damage. I could still hear the screams coming from outside. My panic turned to pure determination as I started the crane up and began to raise it high. The Kaiju hadn't seemed to notice that the crane had started. Its back was to me and it was fixated on the people in front of it. The crane had three pipes at the end of it that we had been using earlier that day for drilling. Each pipe is 45 feet in length and weighs over 2 tons.

What did you do with them?

I dropped it on the fucker's head. [**smiles**] Believe it or not, this thing was still alive too. I dropped three pipes on it, each one hit him, and he was still writhing around, making that horrible hissing noise. Although it was pretty obvious that he was in some pain, I wasn't taking any chances. I raised the crane up once more and brought it down on the snake's head. It didn't kill it, but it sure as shit was making sure he wasn't going anywhere. I jumped out of the crane and asked someone for a gun. Unfortunately, no one had any, so we grabbed some straps and tied it down to the rig.

A few minutes later, the security team from the barge came on board along with a few Pennadime company men. There was a lot of debate as to what we should do with this thing. After reviewing some of the damage, the rig was too banged up to function and we lost too many people to have any hope of salvaging this dig. A lot of us wanted to shoot the damn thing and put an end to it, but the company men seemed to have other plans. They talked about selling the damn thing and putting it on display. That didn't sit right with a lot of the boys. After a little "convincing," we were able to put the creature out of it and our misery.

37 men ended up getting killed by that thing. 37 families that lost a father, husband, or son. There was no way that we were going to let that thing live, regardless of how much money it would be worth. Besides, once the Coast Guard got there, they claimed the body and shut down the rig for further investigation. I still have nightmares about that damn thing. I wake up in the middle of the night with cold

sweats. I keep having the same dream where I'm hitting it with the crane, but nothing seems to be working and it just keeps on coming. It's funny. After the attack happened, I used to think about how unlucky we were to deal with such a creature. That was before the attack on Lord Howe Island, and I saw just how lucky we were that we were only attacked by the baby and not the mother.

AKURRA

Lord Howe Island, Australia

My next interview takes me to Lord Howe Island, a small island that is nearly 400 miles from the Australian coast. This island is well known for its beautiful landscape, indigenous wildlife, and its seclusion from the rest the world. Popular amongst tourists, the island allows no more than 400 people at a time to be on land. At its peak, there were over 300 people living on the island, most of whom can trace their lineage back to the island's original settlers. I am with Mary Smith, an inhabitant and member of the island's seven-person council. Mary, along with the rest of her family, was here when the island came under siege from the Kaiju now known as Akurra. Akurra is believed to be the mother of the creature that

was killed on the oil rig. In this interview, Mary recounts the prolific five days of terror that the island faced under Akurra.

The day was like any other. I woke up, the sun was shining, and the birds were singing. I went to the shop to help my parents for a few hours. We owned a small clothing boutique that was very popular amongst tourists and locals alike. I was there for a few hours before I left to enjoy the day with my friends. A Coast Guard ship arrived to the island sometime in the afternoon, with something large in tow. We knew about the issues with the oil rig, because some of the rig workers were flown here for medical attention. Still, we weren't expecting the ship that was carrying the monster's body to show up at our shores. Apparently, the Coast Guard had gotten word of a small storm that was heading in our direction and didn't want to be at sea when it hit. Their plan was to dock and wait the storm out so that they could get the creature's remains to the researchers in Sydney. Of course, we know that didn't end up happening.

We knew the storm was coming, but its intensity still caught us off guard. One minute, it was warm and sunny out, and the next, there was a torrential downpour. It was still light out, though. That's when we got our first glimpse of Akurra. I remember another boat was en route to the island. It was tourist season, so it wasn't uncommon that we were having a lot of visitors to our shores.

I was sitting on our porch with my friends when we saw something slinking in and out of the water. First, I thought my eyes were playing tricks on me, or that it was just some tidal wave, but then I saw the small ship full of tourists get pulled under the ocean without warning. I wasn't the only one that noticed as a few of us started to walk towards the shore, not entirely sure what we saw. Of course, the Coast Guard was on high alert and began to grab their rescue boats and go towards what remained of the ship. They didn't get very far, though, before they turned right back around and began yelling at everyone on shore. They were waving their arms and I think telling us to run away, but I can't be sure. Whatever they saw was enough to spook them.

Then, like a streak of lightning, we saw Akurra rise up out of the sea where the rescue boats had been. I've never been so awestruck and terrified all at the same time. This thing resembled a sea serpent that you hear about an old mythology stories. Its head was easily 200 feet tall out of the water and that was just the top of it. There was still more of it under the sea. It had two small arms attached to its body, but they looked so disproportionately small to the rest of it that I thought they were fins at first.

The creature seemed to care very little about us though, as it went straight for the Coast Guard ship that had the smaller creature's body on it. Akurra hovered over the ship for some time, nudging at it every so often. I think she was trying to wake it up. Once she realized that her child was dead, Akurra's demeanor changed from almost delicate to animalistic. She raised her head from the ship and began to look at all of us on the island. Her gaze reminded me of a rattlesnake about to strike its prey. Each and every one of us was being held account-able for what happened to her "child." You could see it in her face. She unhinged her jaws and let out a horrible roar, then she began to strike. I don't think she had a specific target in mind, she just started slamming herself against the island, snapping her teeth at anything in front of her. I think she got a few people, but mostly just came away with sand and debris in her mouth. She was just trying to destroy whatever was in her way. She blamed us for the death of her child and we were going to experience all of her fury as a result. People were panicking, running like crazy. Everyone was trying to get away from the shore as fast as possible.

How long did this attack last for?

Hours, she was attacking the coast for hours. Every time she banged her head on the shore, the island trembled. She had circled the island. I don't mean she was swimming around the island, I mean that she literally circled around the island, that's how large she was. At some point during the attack, she decided to throw whatever she could grab in her mouth. This included large chunks of rock, some cars that were parked close to the beach, and all the boats in the harbor. This included the very same boat that her offspring's corpse was on. She just so happened to toss it onto the only runway on the entire Island. That pretty much blocked our only routes of escape. Without the possibility of boat travel or the use of the airfield, we were stuck on the island.

It could've been worse, we could've been without power, then we wouldn't have been able to get in contact with any rescue services. Luckily, with such a small community, we were easily organized and were able to get a crisis response team organized rather quickly. My parents were part of the team that was responsible for triaging some of the people hurt during the chaos. The rest of us spent time organizing the shelter we had set up at the island's school. Lucky for us, the school was located within the island's interior and far away from the coast. We were getting everything set up while a select few people were trying to get some sort of emergency broadcast out to a rescue team. They got in contact with somebody rather quickly, but it wasn't until almost a day later before anyone showed up.

And what did Akurra do during this time?

She continued to molly-whop the coast, just begging for somebody to venture out far enough to get within her grasp. I don't think the rescue teams really comprehended the size of Akurra, because when they first showed up to the island, it was in helicopters. I think they wanted to be able to evacuate the island first. That way they didn't have to worry about civilian casualties when they took the fight to Akurra. The helicopters left from a Navy ship that was floating just a few miles off the coast. It took some tricky maneuvering, but they were able to land on the airfield without hitting any debris. Once the helicopters landed, they received an emergency transmission from the Navy ship they had just departed from. Turns out, Akurra was onto their plan, and she wasn't too happy about it. She attacked that ship and sunk it within a matter of minutes. She was so fast about it that they were barely even able to fire any artillery at her. Whatever shots they did get off did little to no damage. So, now we had helicopters and a few military personnel on the island, but none of the copters had enough fuel to make it back to Sydney. So, we were still stuck, but now we had more tourists. [laughs]

How long did it take before more help arrived this time?

Three days...

Three days? What took so long?

Well, it appeared that the military was either unequipped to deal with such a monster or they wanted more backup. So, it looks like they asked a few allies and the United Nations for some assistance. Akurra had a stranglehold on the island and although we were okay for the time being, our supplies were running low and our options with them. We had quite a few people that were injured in the initial attack and the ones that were still alive needed more medical attention than what we could provide on the island. People often think that things were still hunky-dory, but the reality was we were struggling. To make matters worse, Akurra had taken out power to most of the island when a well-placed Navy boat was thrown onto the island. Any power we had was thanks to some generators and a few solar panels on the island. We needed help and we needed help fast. Akurra was surrounding the island and just waiting for someone to attempt to leave. A few times, we thought she had left, which prompted some brave souls to push a makeshift pontoon into the water. This was quickly swallowed up by a stalking Akurra, who was lying in wait on the ocean floor.

After the three days were over, the military finally showed up?

Pshhh, who didn't show up? We had Australian, American, Japanese, KRSD, and United Nations forces all surrounding our island. Of course, they kept a good distance away from us and waited until an opportune time to strike. Akurra was in the middle of her daily ritual of smashing her head into the shore when, out of nowhere, a missile struck the side of her body. The missile had been fired by the United Nations helicopter which had flown over the island and was now circling back to the horizon. That is when we saw the massive fleet of aircraft and battleships all coming our way.

Akurra, who shook off the hit as though it were nothing, was now looking at the fleet coming directly at her the same way that she looked at us on that first day. She unhinged her jaw again, showing her fangs to the world, and let out another sinister roar. Coincidentally, it started to storm again. I'd read these things can trigger different weather phenomena. I'm not sure if that's what Akurra was doing or not, but it wouldn't surprise me if she did. The storm seemed to match every bit of her fury as she began to swim towards the fleet on the horizon. It was hard for us to see all the action, given how far away we were, but we could sure hear it. Every blast of artillery sent a rumble along the coast, and once the battle really got underway, the island felt like it was in the middle of an earthquake. That is how much artillery was being thrown at this thing, and it just kept on coming. By the end of it, Akurra had destroyed 3 battleships, 5 military aircraft, and injured hundreds more before she succumbed to her wounds and joined her offspring in whatever pit they had crawled out of.

The nightmare was done. We were able to get our injured the help they needed, and it wasn't too long before the island was back to normal. We even gained a spike in tourism when we added the "Akurra attack sites" as part of the island's historic areas. These sites showed some of the devastation she had left in her wake. If you were to see the island now, and how it almost celebrates the monster, you would think that the whole event was nothing more than a mild annoyance, but the reality is that had the military not came when it did, everyone on this island would've died from injuries or starvation. The only benefit that came from that thing showing up on our shores was the influx of tourism.

ON THE DEFENSE

DEFENSE AGAINST THE KAIJU

The old saying "the best offense is a good defense" rings true when discussing Kaiju. These are large and powerful creatures with little to no weaknesses against conventional weapons. When a Kaiju reaches a populated area, it is estimated that 60% of that area's population will be destroyed in the first hour. Unlike natural disasters such as hurricanes or tornadoes, Kaiju are actively seeking human lives to destroy. Their survival depends on it. This chapter will cover how you can better prepare and survive a Kaiju attack, as well as give some pointers on what items you should have with you at all times.

The first Kaiju attack after WWII happened in Japan in 1954. Japan was still recovering from the war, its islands still rural in some parts, with many people living off the sea. Over the weeks leading up to the attacks, three ships had disappeared along the coast. The first two disappeared without so much as a distress call, but the third was a different story. This ship was able to send out a cry for help, with the captain yelling for assistance before he said something about a demon, and then nothing.

These vessels, along with their crew, were never seen again, except for the wreckage that was found. Unfortunately for the

Japanese people, these shipping vessels proved to be just the beginning, as the residents of Tomo Island soon found out.

Tomo Island was a small fishing village that was still very primitive in many ways. While the government was debating what course of action to take based on the limited evidence, the Coast Guard received an S.O.S. from the island's emergency center at approximately 0307 Zulu time. At 0314 Zulu, ships off the coast reported seeing fires on the island. At 0332 Zulu, all contact with the island ceased. The closest ships reported all lights, including the flames, going dark. The sailors on board reported how eerily quiet it was after that. Even the ocean's waves had quieted. Then, the sailors heard a loud roar from the island, something so loud that many of them reported feeling the vibrations of it in their chests. The creature is then believed to have left the island from the north side, opposite of where it arrived. By the time rescuers and first responders arrived, they were shocked at the amount of damage. It looked like a typhoon had hit the island. Debris was everywhere. Skeptics would have been quick to point out this wreckage was the result of a storms, which had been prevalent in the area. There were a few abnormalities, however, that researchers just couldn't ignore.

The first were the discernible footprints that couldn't have been caused by any weather phenomena. The second was the state of the villagers' remains. Researchers found very few remains of any sort, but the ones they did find had obviously been pulled or torn apart by something of immense size.

These findings, among others, were enough to make Japanese officials take these attacks seriously. 270 lives vanished on Tomo Island that night, something that many believe could have been avoided if the government had acted sooner.

Regardless of these accusations, the events of Tomo Island shook the Japanese government to its core. They formed a research team with the intention of preparing for and ultimately destroying this terrible creature. This early research team was the first iteration of the KRSD. The monster eventually emerged once again, this time off the shores of Tokyo. Only this time, the Japanese were prepared.

After a long and destructive battle that lasted over a full day, the Kaiju was eliminated by the Japanese.

The emergence of this creature led to some of the top Japanese researchers to develop contingency plans should such a creature ever appear again. In America, however, we were not taking such threats seriously. The country had just won the war and was finding its place in the world. This talk of a new monster, potentially a result of nuclear fallout, ruffled the feathers of Americans and Japanese alike. The American government was watching the situation closely but was ultimately waiting for it to die down so we could move on and sweep this atomic mess under the rug. That, unfortunately, never happened.

In the summer of 1954, just months after the attack in Japan, America dealt with its first major Kaiju attack that, to this day, remains terrifying to think about.

Researchers in the New Mexico desert had been looking into unusual seismic activity. These readings were coming directly from the blast sites of the first nuclear tests conducted during WWII. When researchers arrived on-scene, they found tunnels underground. These tunnels were vast and believed to go for miles. Scientists were instantly puzzled by the sudden appearance of such caves and how they never noticed them before the nuclear testing. They soon found their answer as more seismic activity exposed the creators. Before they knew it, researchers were overrun by a colony of giant ants measuring eight feet high. These ants attacked the researchers with a fury, grabbing and crushing them with their impressive power. Fortunately, three researchers were able to escape. Two of the researchers survived their injuries and were able to warn the government. The third unfortunately succumbed to the acidic wounds inflicted upon him by the ants, but his sacrifice was not in vain. Researchers were able to study his wounds to better understand what they were dealing with.

When the military arrived to deal with the threat, they were met with little resistance. This puzzled researchers, who reported a massive colony in the original attack. It wasn't long until the government realized that the colony was on the move. Since her last colony had been disturbed, the queen was leading her children to a new location. The military tried to keep all this quiet so it wouldn't cause a panic, but that didn't last long. The ants began to venture towards more populated areas, attacking anything in sight. Once investigators thought they had a radius locked down for a possible nest, they used a seismograph to help track the ants' movements. Their worst fears were eventually confirmed that the ant colony had moved its nest to right under the city of Albuquerque. These ants wasted no time in establishing their new colony and attacked any life form deemed too close to the queen's location. Most of the city was in danger and martial law was declared.

The military soon arrived, and the new nest was eventually destroyed thanks to a combination of gas and flamethrowers, but the damage had already been done. Hundreds of people lost their lives in the first few days of infestation, all because the government didn't want to cause a panic.

These two attacks are some of the most devastating Kaiju attacks in human history. The lack of communication and failure to notify the civilians in a timely matter cost both countries hundreds of lives. Additionally, these attacks, in such a short span of time from one another, put the rest of the world on notice. The United Nations soon called an emergency meeting amongst its members to discuss this new threat and how to better deal with it. They put a team together of the world's top zoologists, biologists, and other scientists to investigate what these creatures were, what they wanted, and how we could stop them. Additionally, each country was encouraged to develop their own emergency notification system to warn its civilians in a timely manner.

Unfortunately, Japan was not at this UN summit, as they did not join the UN until 1956. They had their own issues during this time, including two additional Kaiju attacks, similar to the first sea creature they dealt with in 1954. With much respect to the Japanese, they dealt with these two attacks quickly and fiercely as to not have another incident like the one on Tomo Island. The Japanese developed their own special research division to combat the Kaiju menace and in 1955, the Kaiju Research and Survival Department (KRSD) was born.

This force, originally composed of Japan's greatest minds and soldiers alike, is still the world's leading force in research and defense against the Kaiju. Today, the KRSD is an entity that works with the governments of the world to help stop the Kaiju menace.

The KRSD is an independent agency within the United Nations. Japan's joining the UN allowed to world's foremost Kaiju experts to finally interact with the rest of the world. This meeting eventually gave birth to the Kayama Protocols. These rules and regulations, which are still in use today, help dictate what civilians and military should do during a Kaiju attack. These protocols are the main focus of this chapter to help you and your loved ones survive the Kaiju menace.

WARNING SIGNS

The first and possibly most important thing to watch for are the warning signs. Although Kaiju can appear without warning sometimes, the signs are almost always there as long as you know what to look for. This section discusses these signs and how you can be aware of them.

1. ENVIRONMENTAL CHANGES

Kaiju are unnatural beasts living in a world not meant to support them. Their travel disturbs everything in their path. Few Kaiju have ever understood the concept of stealth, which, believe it or not, is a benefit to us. When a Kaiju travels, whether by land, sea, or air, it often leaves some sort of wreckage in its wake. This can include massive footprints, downed trees, or massive tidal waves. This world is not big enough for the Kaiju, and so these signs of disturbance can often be an early warning sign of an arriving Kaiju. If you encounter a disturbed area with signs of Kaiju movement, calmly proceed to your nearest safe zone and inform the authorities.

2. WILDLIFE

Kaiju have no preference when they are looking for food. Their only goal is to replenish their energy. This can also be a warning sign, especially if the Kaiju is on the smaller side. These Kaiju will usually be obvious if they are on land, as they will still attack large groups of animals, including bears, moose, or livestock. It all depends on the location of the Kaiju. Aquatic Kaiju will often go after sharks, whales, or any large school of fish. Probably the hardest Kaiju to track in this method are the Aero Class Kaiju, who, like other birds of prey, often snatch their food from the sky and carry it off to be eaten elsewhere.

Animals have shown to be very receptive to a Kaiju's presence. Some farmers report livestock refusing to come out of their barn to graze. Fishermen have reported similar cases where fish have seemingly disappeared overnight or whole fishing cages have been destroyed without a trace. These can all be indications of a Kaiju in the area and should be reported immediately.

3. WEATHER

This phenomenon is unproven as of yet but will still be included to allow you to make an informed decision. Some of the most powerful Kaiju we have encountered have had some type of weather phenomenon precede them. Often when a Kaiju emerges, it can cause damage to the environment, such as earthquakes or tidal waves. The meteorological phenomena we are discussing here is something more severe, with Kaiju almost appearing to summon severe weather conditions like that of a hurricane or blizzard. The weather doesn't follow the Kaiju but instead seems to foreshadow it.

To date, there has never been any indication that a Kaiju can control the weather, but these sudden storms baffle meteorologists. Whether it is somehow linked to the Kaiju's nuclear origins, such as the planet reacting to such an extreme creature, or some mystical ability is unknown at this time.

4. EMERGENCY BROADCASTS

This is how the majority of civilians receive news on a possible Kaiju attack. In the event a Kaiju is sighted, the emergency broadcast network will inform civilians using television, radio, and text. Much like a storm warning, this will consist of a loud audible alarm followed by the information available. There is also an available app for your phone that will notify you about Kaiju activity in your area. This is the primary way that the emergency broadcasts are distributed, but it is still important to always be on the lookout for the other warning signs listed above, as a powerful Kaiju may destroy emergency broadcast centers or other power sources.

SAFE LOCATIONS

One of the best things to come out of the Kayama Protocols was the necessity for safe zones. These zones are created primarily for those that live in populated areas such as cities or large towns. Although they exist in other areas as well, they are not as common in rural parts of the world. The safe zones in each city are marked on any city map. These safe zones cannot be visited unless there is a legitimate Kaiju threat, otherwise they stay locked to the public.

The average safe zone is located at least 50 feet below ground in a hardened bunker. These bunkers vary in size depending on location, with the largest ones being able to successfully house and feed 500 individuals for up to two weeks. Once locked down, these bunkers can only be accessed from key locations. During a Kaiju attack, one wants to be as low to the ground as possible. Kaiju will go through any obstacle they think is in their way. If a Kaiju attacks a large city, the first thing to go are the buildings throughout the concrete jungle. This is primarily why the bunkers are built so low. Should a Kaiju terrorize the city, it is unlikely it would burrow so deep underground, but just in case, the bunkers are built to withstand severe damage. These bunkers are reportedly strong enough to withstand a barrage from military warheads. Some bunkers have all the amenities of home, including private rooms, food, water, and even limited electronics use. Many high-end apartment buildings have started building their own bunkers for their residents. These bunkers are by all accounts much nicer than the ones allotted to the public, but they contribute to the price point for real estate within the city. Regardless of the shelter you choose to take, it is important to remember to watch for the signs of a Kaiju attack and always have an escape route. That expensive apartment in the city isn't worth the price point if you cannot reach its bunker in a timely manner.

PRIVATE RESIDENCE

This section is for those that live in more rural areas or areas not very close to an underground bunker. If you do not have access to a personal bunker, then you are faced with two options.

OPTION ONE

Stay put and barricade yourself in your house. Much like in the event of a tornado or other storm, try to get to a basement or bathroom and secure yourself and your family members there. Avoid making noise at all costs. Kaiju have been shown to have a very keen sense of smell, but their other senses aren't so bad either. If you are able to coat the outside of your house in bleach, then do so. Studies have shown that Kaiju hate the smell of chemicals, especially ammonia. This is common practice hunters use, spraying ammonia to keep predators away from certain areas. The spraying of bleach (or other household chemicals) has been shown to cover the smell of humans and cause Kaiju to move on to the next location.

It is important to have food and other supplies readily available in your house should you need to stay for an extended period. It is recommended to have at least two weeks' worth of supplies for each person in your household.

OPTION TWO

Run!

Not literally of course, but if you do not have faith in your present location as a safe haven, then you need to get to a new location ASAP. Depending on your location, this can prove to be a problem in and of itself. Although cities have underground bunkers, they cannot fit everyone in them. Some cities like Detroit only have three bunkers for a city with over half a million residents. When a Kaiju warning is in place, many people will be trying to exit the city. This will cause mass panic, with many of the city's exits being clogged with traffic. If you are unable to get to someplace quick, then you need to find a dependable vehicle that will get you to safety without the worry of getting stuck out in the open. We will go over recommended vehicles later in this book, but regardless of your choice, it is important you keep it in proper condition or at the very least have some basic automotive knowledge should you need to make any repairs.

MAKING A FORTRESS/BUNKER

Many people around the world have decided to build their own underground shelters to survive the Kaiju menace. This is very admirable and is highly recommended if you have the funds to do so. This section will detail the use of shelters, some basic knowledge on building them, and what necessities you need for your personal use.

1. SHELTER COST

The cost of building a personal shelter can vary wildly depending on the type you want to build, its amenities, and even location. Building a shelter into a mountainside will cost more than building one underground. As for bare minimum, it is possible to build a shelter without spending more than $2,500 U.S. This cheap method would involve digging a hole no less than three feet below the surface and using a tarp or large piece of wood to cover the top of the hole. The rest of the cost would go to supplies such as water and food. This may be ideal for a makeshift bunker during a chemical strike, but would not offer the security needed if a Kaiju were to attack. For a quality shelter, capable of safely protecting you and your family, you can expect to spend at least $50,000.

2. GETTING STARTED

When establishing the location of your shelter, you first want to make sure it is away from any trees or large rock formations. These can make it extremely difficult to dig into the ground and would waste valuable time and energy. You want to build on a flat surface that is no less the three feet deep into the ground. The reason for this is that in the event of nuclear fallout, it takes approximately three feet of earth to absorb 99% of the gamma radiation. You will want to build a shelter deeper than that if you can.

This shelter should be built within close proximity to your home but not directly connected to it. Should anything happen to your home while you are trying to escape, the debris could block you from reaching safety. Additionally, you are less likely to risk debris falling on top of the shelter and trapping you in if it is away from trees and other structures. Your shelter should be incased in thick concrete walls that can protect you and your loved ones from debris, radiation, and Kaiju movement.

3. POWERING YOUR SHELTER

Ideally, you should not have to stay in your shelter for more than two weeks. This is the estimated amount of time it would take a Kaiju to die if it cannot get the nourishment it needs to survive. However, it is best to prepare for the worst-case scenario and hope for the best rather then not at all. For this reason, we will go in depth about the different methods of powering your shelter.

SOLAR PANELS

While not completely useless, solar panels are vulnerable to solar flares. You would also have to leave these panels out in the open, which could be a problem with a rampaging monster destroying everything in sight. A panel's output is also affected by the amount of sunlight in a given area. This isn't a problem for most areas other than the far north, but if a Kaiju appears that is able to trigger weather phenomena, then the panels could prove useless. All the risks aside though, solar panels are still very useful if coupled with another power source. Hooking the panels up away from the shelter is your best call. Always have at least one solar panel safely in storage so that you can replace the one outside if it gets damaged or destroyed. This solar panel should be should be wrapped in foil in order to better protect it from EMPs.

GENERATORS

A generator is one of the more efficient power sources for your shelter. A diesel generator specifically has been proven as very efficient and isn't susceptible to EMPs. The issues with generators, however, make them a last resort for anyone needing to stay underground for long. Generators can be loud, even when they are ten feet underground. If the shelter is not noise-proof, then this could attract the unwanted attention of Kaiju and looters alike. The other issue is finding enough fuel to power the generator. In an evacuation, food and fuel are the first things to go, so it is encouraged you have fuel stored before an attack happens. This way, should you need to use the generator, you do not have to worry about it running out. The type of generator you have will determine just how much fuel you should have on hand.

WIND TURBINES

Wind turbines are not the best source of power in the best of conditions. For the use of a private shelter, they would not be able to produce an efficient amount of power to be useful. Having wind turbines out in the open face the same risks as solar panels in terms of exposure.

BATTERIES

A powerful enough battery can be used to power a small shelter for up to three weeks. This method, if set up correctly, can be the most efficient form of power. Any good shelter should have a large supply of batteries, preferably rechargeable, that can be used to power both the shelter and its appliances. A useful setup is having the batteries hooked up to the outside solar panel so that they can get a charge from the solar energy. Many homeowners go with a 12 or 48-volt system, depending on their shelter's size and budget. The 12-volt system is more cost effective, with less expensive chargers and inverters. Gel cell batteries seem to be the most efficient as they require little maintenance, can be configured in more diverse ways, and will recharge more quickly than the conventional lead acid batteries.

4. HEATING/VENTILATION

Proper ventilation is a must for any survival shelter. Human beings give off immense amounts of heat and water vapor that, in an enclosed area, could prove fatal. For this and other reasons, a ventilation system of some sort is an absolute necessity for your Kaiju shelter. If time and money allow, you should invest in an air conditioner that possesses a filter. Any air system is going to take air from the outside world and funnel it into your shelter, which makes the risk of radiation exposure a real one. A simple air filter system should help to eliminate any potential risk while the radiation dies down. Radioactive particles are too large to fall into air vents and since the soil will absorb the majority of the radiation, a filter is not necessary but still highly encouraged. For those of us that lack the funds or time for a quality air system, there are other options as well. Manmade fans such as a KAP air pump would be enough to circulate air in small spaces. The danger with these systems is their need for manpower in order to work. This means the shelter's air flow depends entirely on the individuals living inside of it and their physical stamina. Survivors will have to take turns in order to keep the air flow manageable.

5. WATER

A healthy adult human can survive up to two weeks without food but only a few days without water. This is why water usage and consumption should be one of the most important things to consider when building a Kaiju shelter. Water, like fuel and food, should be stored regularly in your shelter well before an attack. The average shelf life of store-bought water is five years, however, scientists recommend rotating the water in storage with the water you use every six months. This way there is a constant supply of usable water on hand so that if a Kaiju does attack, you are able to hold out in your shelter for as long as necessary. Water is one of the first things to disappear in the event of an emergency, so it is a good idea to have some on hand at all times.

When calculating the amount of water to have, assume that each person requires a gallon of water per day. Although you can buy water bottles in bulk, it is recommended that you do not store them in your shelter as it will take up more space and create more waste in the long run. Instead, you should purchase at least one water drum that can hold a minimum of five gallons. These drums will store your water and take up less space. Some preppers will hook up multiple water tanks to different parts of the shelter for things such as personal hygiene, bathroom uses, or cleaning. If you fear the water is contaminated with bacteria, remember that you can always treat the water by boiling, hand pump, chemical, or ultraviolet filtration. Regardless of where and how it is stored, the water needs to be easily accessible to all members in the shelter.

6. HYGIENE

When living is close quarters with other human beings, good hygiene is a necessity. Failure to keep yourself and your area clean can lead to disease and mental stability issues. It is recommended that each survivor has their own washcloth, toothbrush, and cup that they use for cleaning themselves. One cup of water a day should be enough for each member to clean themselves. You can use the washcloth to clean yourself more thoroughly and make more use of the cup of water. It is recommended that each shelter has some sort of cleaning area that can be used for hygiene and laundering clothing. It is preferable to clean everyone's cloths at once so that you use less water overall. In order to mitigate the spread of disease, each individual should have their own cup, plate, bowl, and eating utensils that they can use for food. This will help prevent the spread of disease, mitigate the use of water, and also hold everyone accountable for rationing supplies.

7. FOOD

When storing food for long-term shelter survival, some experts will advise you to get a years' worth of food. This is simply not practical and is advice that should not be followed. Some survivalists advise freezers that you can store large amounts of meat in and while this is certainly an option, a long-term diet of such food will cause havoc on your digestive tract. Three months' worth of food should be your goal. Your shelter food should be a combination of canned and boxed goods, along with dry grains, pasta, and legumes. The reason for this is that canned/boxed goods usually have a much longer shelf life than other foods. As far as the pasta and other foods go, they are rich in calories, which is what the human body needs for survival. These calories will provide the survivors with enough sustenance while they are waiting for the all clear. It is important to grab foods that you enjoy but will also provide you with enough nutrients to stay active. For example, if you run out of meat, a good substitute is beans which, like meat, are rich in protein. Many survivalists also recommend Meals Ready to Eat (MREs), a meal on the go that many members of the military eat when in combat environments. Each MRE possesses a minimum of 1200 calories and has a shelf life of at least three years. These meals are incredibly durable, and are even capable of withstanding para-chute drops from up to 1250 feet. These meals can be bought in bulk and have a variety of contents from tuna and crackers to spaghetti.

8. WASTE

Humans create a massive amount of waste just by existing, with the average person generating 4.4 pounds of waste each day. This becomes a serious issue when you consider the situation in a Kaiju shelter. Any shelter should have cleaning supplies to combat the issue of sanitation. The most popular method of waste disposal is to create a waste area close to the air exhaust of your shelter so the smell does not become unbearable. This area should have a waste container of some sort that you can store garbage in. You do not want it to be too big since you will more than likely need to empty it outside of your shelter. While this can create a danger in itself, the alternative is laying in your own filth and facing disease. Dumping your waste should be a quick process, not taking more than a few seconds.

Before exiting your shelter, it is important you ensure that Kaiju and looters are nowhere near, as your sudden appearance could put the rest of the residents of the shelter at risk.

You should avoid any insect sprays within the shelter, as they can be dangerous to humans. Instead use fly bait or screens and place them next to your air system.

Plastic bags will also be very useful, not just for transporting waste, but also in the unfortunate event of death. These bags can be used to transport the deceased outside of the shelter until proper burial can be arranged. You do not want to keep a dead body within your shelter as it can potentially cause disease.

9. HAZARDS

While Kaiju shelters are great for keeping safe during a Kaiju attack, they are not invincible and are susceptible to dangers like any other location. This section will look at the common dangers facing any Kaiju shelter and the ways you can possibly protect yourself from them.

EMP/SOLAR FLARE

EMPs and solar flares have been talked about at length in this book. They are a huge danger that can potentially destroy any and all power sources within your shelter. It is important that your shelter not be hooked up to a power grid. If a Kaiju possesses strong enough EMP abilities and damages the grid, anything connected to it could potentially be destroyed. For this reason, you want your shelter hooked up to other power sources such as solar panels, batteries, or a generator. When not in use, it is important to keep electronics shut off. This seems to protect them somewhat from EMP attacks. Another technique used by many preppers is the construction of a faraday cage. A faraday cage is a metal screen meant to conduct electricity and absorb EMP energy, creating a shielding effect. A faraday cage is very simple to make and can range in size, making it the ideal protection from EMP-capable Kaiju.

RADIATION

A Nuclear Kaiju would cause more havoc to mankind then most natural disasters. If one should ever emerge, it is important that your shelter have proper defense against the radiation that these Kaiju would produce. This isn't some bomb going off in the sky or on impact, this is a giant, walking nuclear warhead with near infinite power. If a Kaiju fires a nuclear blast directly over your shelter, it is unlikely that you, or anything within a mile radius, would survive unless you are very deep underground. Should you be safely out of the blast radius, you would still need to combat the dangers of radiation. Luckily, the ground will absorb most radiation and it is unlikely radioactive debris could affect your ventilation system. It is of the utmost importance that each shelter have the following for each of its members:

-**RADIATION SUIT:** Should include a jacket, hood, gloves, boots, and M8/M9 paper worn on the suit.

-**GASMASK:** A quality gasmask should be properly sized and have a firm seal to your face. It is important you have it on hand during Kaiju attacks.

-**POTASSIUM IODIDE TABLETS:** These tablets help to prevent thyroid cancer, a common side effect of nuclear radiation.

-**RADIATION DETECTOR:** An electronic sensor that measures nuclear radiation in the area. Make sure it is battery-powered and fully charged.

-**M8 PAPER:** A piece of paper that can detect liquid agents and changes to red, green, or yellow, depending on the compound detected.

-**M9 PAPER:** A piece of paper that detects liquid nerve and blister agents by turning red in color, though doesn't distinguish which is which.

FLOODING

Flooding is a real danger to all homes, and shelters are no exception to that. When building your shelter, it is important to build it in an elevated area that is not prone to floods. You should also avoid living close to the water, as 70% of Kaiju emerge from a body of water and cause tidal waves or flooding in the process. If you live next to a body of water or an area that is prone to flooding, you may want to consider moving. Even if the shelter does not flood, the water above-ground could have enough pressure to prevent you from opening your escape door. This would create a watery grave for everyone inside the shelter.

FIRE

Fire is a very real danger no matter the location. It is important that each shelter be equipped with fire extinguishers that are checked regularly. These extinguishers should be kept in an easy to reach location in at least both ends of the shelter. A fireproof blanket is also recommended, as it can help control the blaze. Avoid using water unless absolutely necessary, as this will hurt your water supply. Should a fire get out of control, the residents will need to evacuate for their own safety. You should also have burn kits on hand in case of both fire and nuclear burns.

QUICK LIST OF ITEMS INSIDE YOUR BUNKER
- **FOOD**
- **WATER**
- **LIGHT STICKS**
- **RADIATION PROTECTION (listed above)**
- **5 GALLON BUCKETS**
- **PORTABLE TOILET (optional)**

- PLASTIC WASTE BAGS
- BLEACH
- FIRST AID KIT
- MEDICAL TOOLS
- NON-PRESCRIPTION DRUGS (painkiller, fever reliever, etc.,)
- TOOLS
- CLOTHES
- BEDDING
- BUG-OUT BAG
- ADDITIONAL ITEMS (medications, wills, cash, entertainment)

DEFENDING YOUR FORTRESS

Having a Kaiju shelter gives you an added protection during a period of absolute chaos, but it does not make you or your loved ones invincible. We often speak of the worst-case scenario when describing a Kaiju attack, and while it is good to plan for a Category V Kaiju, it is more than likely not ever going to be a reality. The most common Kaiju attacks are those in Category III and below, meaning the monsters are smaller. Although they still possess immense power, it is unlikely one would be able to penetrate a secure shelter.

Unfortunately, Kaiju are not the only threat you will face during an attack. People do crazy things when they are trying to survive, especially if they are desperate. People will be wanting food, shelter, and other supplies both during and after a Kaiju attack, making you a prime target for looters. If possible, it is recommended that you keep your shelter secret from anyone outside of your immediate household for this very reason. The less people that know about the shelter, the less likely they are to attack. While you do not have to turn away every person that comes asking for help, just remember that each individual brings with them an additional mouth to feed. Unless you have overstocked your supplies, this will be a huge hit to your resources and present new issues in hygiene and available space.

Whether it is Kaiju or looters trying to break into your shelter, it is important to have proper defenses. This means anything from firearms to booby traps. Before setting up any security system, it is very important to be familiar with the laws in your part of the world, as different countries and even different states all have different laws regarding defense. The traps you set up should be well hidden and pose no danger to yourself or your loved ones. It is a good idea to set up a trap near the entrance of the shelter. Some survivalists set up a spraying mechanism that they use as a non-lethal way to mace or gas. The main goal should be to keep anyone (or anything) from getting into your shelter. Should the traps not keep away the enemy, the next form of defense is the use of firearms.

Earlier in this book, we described the different functions for each type of firearm. Whatever you choose, it is important that you know how to handle such a weapon safely and possess enough ammunition for it as well. Other weapons such as bludgeons or blades are effective as well. You will want to avoid the use of any explosives such as grenades or flamethrowers as you run the risk of damaging your shelter and potentially needing to evacuate, as any smoke could cause suffocation. If all else fails, then your last resort is to retreat.

RETREAT

You should have an exit to your shelter, other than the entrance, that is easily accessible in case of emergencies. Gather your prepared supplies and your loved ones and run. Exiting your shelter should be an absolute last resort but a possibility you must be prepared for at all times. Each member of your shelter should have traveling attire appropriate for the terrain of your area. They should also have some sort of weapon that they are properly trained to use, as well as a bug-out bag. The next chapter will discuss the supplies needed for each individual and tips for surviving out in the open.

LIVING AT SEA

Living at sea can seem attractive to some. The abundance of ocean life and resources could make aquatic survival more manageable then other environments, but the major drawback to the ocean is that it is swarming with Kaiju. The KRSD isn't exactly sure what the reason is for so much Kaiju activity in the sea. It could be easier living conditions for them as the ocean water puts less stress on their large bodies, or perhaps it is the abundance of sea life for these monsters to eat. Whatever the reason, one thing is clear, the ocean is their domain. The sections below will offer general details about the types of boats available, what essential gear you should have on your watercraft, and how to defend yourself at sea from Kaiju and people alike.

It cannot be stressed enough, however, that you should avoid the water at all costs. Do not go into the ocean unless it is your absolute last resort. The emergence of Kaiju has changed our world's economy so much due to them attacking large shipping vessels. As a result, the world's navies have almost tripled in size, with a focus on patrolling our waters for Kaiju, but even they have a hard time keeping the seas safe. Approach any type of aquatic travel with the utmost caution.

BOATS

This section lists the three basic types of boats, how they are powered, and the usefulness they would have in Kaiju-infested waters.

SAILBOATS

Mankind has used wind to help it tame the seas for centuries. Although overshadowed by faster vessels, a sailboat can still be useful in today's waters. Powered by wind instead of fuel, these boats never run out of gas, being only limited by nature itself. Sailboats are quiet, which is good for not drawing the attention of any sea monsters. That being said, sailing can be very physically demanding and will require a skilled group to work as a team. Most sailboats are typically smaller then motorboats, and they will force you to be exposed to the elements more than if you were on a motorboat. The other problem with these boats is the sail maintenance. Sails can get torn or ripped easily if exposed to harsh conditions, and this can put an end to travel if you do not have the proper repair kits or replacement sails. Luckily, most sailboats will also have a small propeller they can switch on for travel, but the fuel these boats can hold is significantly smaller than their counterparts. If you are looking for stealth, and you are an experienced sailor, then a sailboat may be for you.

MOTORBOATS

Motorboats are gas-powered boats that allow for more room and faster travel then most other watercraft. Limited only by the amount of fuel they can carry, these boats start out at 6 knots (the max speed for most sailboats). These boats are easy to start and require little knowledge on how to drive them. They are more spacious then other craft, and they allow for the storage of food and other resources. The drawbacks to these craft are their fuel dependency and the amount of noise they generate. Kaiju are attracted to noise, and these boats have plenty of it. A faster boat usually means a louder boat. These vessels are ideal if someone needs to make a quick escape and have enough room for their whole group to travel.

UNPOWERED BOATS

Unpowered boats, also known as man-powered boats, are watercraft that are not powered by either wind or fuel but by its passengers. This includes rowboats and paddleboats. These types of boats should be avoided at all costs. The only reason you should ever attempt travel in this type of boat is because your other boat sank. These boats are slow, typically have poor maneuvering, and are usually quite small. Additionally, they offer little to no protection from the elements and should never be used for extended travel at sea. Avoid these boats at all cost.

ESSENTIALS

The following are just some essentials to have while at sea. This list goes with the other list of resources in the "Equipment/Supplies" section of the Escape/Survival chapter. While you can add to this list as you see fit, these items should be essential for each watercraft you have.

-**Flare Gun: This is** essential for a rescue.

-**Paddles:** If all else fails, these will come in handy. Although you can't use them for a large boat, you will want them on hand should you need to use the life raft.

-**Fuel:** If your boat runs on fuel, then you will want a few extra fuel stores in case of emergency.

-**Sunscreen/lip balm:** This cannot be stressed enough. Out on the open ocean, there is little to no protection from the sun other than your boat. Should something happen to your boat, you will be exposed to the elements. This can lead to extreme sunburn/poisoning. Use these as needed to protect yourself.

-**Flashlight:** This will come in handy at nighttime or in case your vessel loses power.

-**Batteries:** Bring enough batteries for any and all electronic devices.

-**Anchors and Line**

-**Manual Bailer:** A bailer is used to pump water out of the boat. Should your vessel take on any water, this will be a useful tool.

-**Food & Water:** Self-explanatory, but bring enough food and water for however long you are planning to be at sea.

-**Life Raft:** Absolutely essential in case your vessel becomes damaged. You should also have a life raft repair kit with you.

-**Fire Extinguisher**

-**Personal Floatation Devices (PFD):** Should you be trapped at sea and exposed to the harsh elements, these floatation devices may be all that keeps you from drowning.

-**VHF Radio:** This radio can be used to communicate with first responders and other vessels.

-**Thermal Cameras:** Good for traveling at night, these cameras will help you see any obstacles or potential Kaiju when visibility is bad.

-**Motion Sickness Pills:** Sea travel can be rough at times, so these are always good to have on hand during the worst weather conditions.

-**Hats/Face Protection:** Like the sunscreen, these will add extra protection from the sun.

-**Fishing Gear:** If the worst should happen and you run out of food at sea, fishing will become your only option for food.

-**Bait**

-**Fish Cleaning Tools**

-**First Aid Kit**

-**Appropriate Travel Documents:** This includes license, passport, and anything else you may need for documentation while traveling.

-**Toiletries/Hygiene:** Toilet paper, soap, shampoo, conditioner, toothbrush, and anything else to make your time at sea more bearable.

-**Appropriate Clothing:** Dress for your climate.

-**Cold Weather Gear:** It gets cold at night, make sure you have clothes that will be able to keep you warm.

-**Blankets:** Something that will keep you warm and that you are able to dry off in should you go overboard unexpectedly.

-**Scuba Equipment:** In case you need to leave the boat to make any repairs, make sure you have proper scuba gear, including goggles, snorkels, scuba tanks, flippers, and wetsuit.

DEFENDING YOUR VESSEL

Below is a small list of weapons/tools that are used to defend watercraft from pirates on the open seas. While almost none of these weapons would prove useful against Kaiju, it is still important to cover this section so that you are prepared for the worst. Unfortunately, Kaiju are not the only predator at sea. Pirates still terrorize the ocean in different parts of the world. If the civil unrest Kaiju create continues to increase, then it can only be assumed that the pirates will continue to grow in number. These tools only apply to civilian vessels. No military weapons are mentioned in this section due to their unavailability for civilian watercraft.

FIREARMS

These are the most obvious way to defend your vessel from unwanted attention. While guns could be quite effective against pirates, and most sea life, they won't do much against the Kaiju. These are still good to have on hand and can always be useful for self-defense.

GRENADES

A grenade, whether it's a stun grenade or explosive grenade, would do quite a bit against pirates.

TASERS

While good for defending yourself in close quarters, a taser would do little for you on the open sea. Unless the intruders are already on your vessel, then you will likely not even be able to get within range to fire your taser. There is also the fact that most pirates are well armed, meaning that a firearm may be a better alternative.

SAFEROOM

If you prefer a non-lethal approach, you can always set up a saferoom within your vessel. When danger approaches, these rooms can be used by your group to stay securely inside while the pirates come aboard. You should be able to use the radio to call for help while in this room. Use caution with this, however, as you are still at sea. Although this safe room may be protected, the boat is not. Pirates can still sink your vessel and force you to evacuate from safety.

ELECTRIC FENCE/LIFELINES

Some experienced sailors will wrap their vessel in an electrified fence that can give a painful shock to anyone that attempts to come aboard. The shock is typically non-lethal, and sometimes does little more than aggravate attackers, but it should prevent them from boarding your vessel. A Kaiju might not enjoy the fence and could destroy your vessel out of frustration.

HIGH-ENERGY RADIO FREQUENCY (HERF) GUN

The HERF gun is gaining much popularity in the nautical community. Used primarily by the military, these guns are becoming available on the market and are being bought by sailors all over the world. A HERF gun fires a non-lethal narrow beam of electromagnetic energy that can heat a person's skin from hundreds of meters away. These guns are not only gaining popularity against pirates but also Kaiju. Boats will shoot these beams at a Kaiju spotted in the distance as a means of deterring it from getting closer. For the most part, these guns seem to work quite well, but every so often, you do hear about a particularly tough Kaiju that only seems aggravated by the gun.

WATER HOSE

Another non-lethal way to deter anyone boarding your vessel is by shooting a high-powered water hose in their direction. Of course, this doesn't do much good if the person is armed.

INDRIK

KRSD US Headquarters, Tampa, Florida

The events in Russia that took place in 2012 have intrigued scientists and researchers all over the world, but none more than those of the KRSD. We do not know much, but what we do now is that a meteor hit the area of Lake Chebarkul at exactly 03:20 UTC. Precisely six hours after the initial impact, news outlets reported earthquakes in the area. Two hours after that, we have the first confirmed sighting of the creature now known as Indrik. Although the details are sketchy at best, what we do know is that this creature went on a two-day rampage through the countryside. It seemed to have no purpose or goal other than destruction. Russian officials have kept most of details secret, with the little bit that we do have coming from eyewitnesses and the occasional reporter. Even now, we are not sure if the meteor and the creature known as

Indrik share any connection, although our researchers have their own theories on that matter. Indrik was eventually put down, but not before exhausting almost every weapon in the Russian military's arsenal, with the exception of nuclear warheads. The following is an eyewitness account of Indrik's rampage from a prison doctor whose devotion to duty led her to stay behind to care for the inmates when no one else would.

Looking back at everything, it is still astounding to me that they did not evacuate the facility sooner. I understand that it is a prison and is full of society's less desirables, but the fact remains that these were still human beings. It was not until the creature was only 20 miles away, far too close for us to hope to evacuate in time. Once the call was finally made, the warden began to load up the prisoners onto buses, but those were in limited supply due to the other evacuations taking place within the city. In the end, only a quarter of the prisoners were evacuated while the rest were left to rot. This understandably upset many of the prisoners and led to a prison riot.

How did you stay safe during the riot?

Luckily, the medical wing was able to be locked down in time. The only people in the wing at that time were myself, Sergei, the older guard that was posted to our wing, one nurse named Lyndsay, and the six patients we were attending to. Four of the prisoners were restrained due to their violent behavior. Another patient was a regular, always faking some injury in an attempt to get drugs. The sixth patient was an unfortunate victim of a brutal gang attack. He had been in a medically-induced coma for the last few days due to his injuries.

Did you have any way of knowing what was going on outside the medical wing?

Each guard station had cameras that showed us the inside and outside of key points around the prison. We had a guard station in the medical wing, which was both good and bad. Good in the fact that we were aware of what was happening outside of our doors, and bad in the way that we knew what was happening outside of our doors. I will skip the nasty details, but the prisoners clearly had a lot pent-up frustration and outnumbered the small unit of guards that was left within the walls.

So, the prisoners essentially took over the prison?

Not exactly. Even the monsters in our walls knew they were no match for what was coming towards us. The vast majority of the prisoners escaped after the riot. The ones that stayed behind did so because they saw no other option, or at least that's what we thought at first.

Did they try to get into the medical wing?

Not at first, no. First, they went around the prison to release any inmates that had been kept in their cells during the evacuation. This included some fairly violent offenders, war criminals, and the death row inmates. It was only after creating this small army that they came to the medical wing. This wasn't surprising at all. It is quite common for prisoners to try and steal medical supplies from our wing. Most of them are recovering (and failing) drug addicts that are looking for anything to get them high. On top of that, myself and the nurse were the only two females in the prison. This led to a lot of unwanted attention. I'm not sure if that was a motivating factor, but it did come up during their threats. Still though, we were fairly confident they wouldn't be able to get in. The doors were secure and the only way to open them was from our side. Try and threaten as they might, there was no way they were getting in.

What changed?

Well, unfortunately, we did not account for the prisoners we had with us. Our regular visitor, Andrei, constantly had stomach pain or any other illness that he could come up with on that day. The other three were there because they were hurt fighting each other. They were all restrained though, so we didn't think too much of it. The only way that they were getting out of those restraints was if myself or my staff let them out, and given the state of things, I didn't feel like dealing with any more inmates. Unfortunately for us, Andrei had a different set of plans. It may sound stupid now, but we grew to trust certain inmates to an extent. Infirmary regulars like Andrei were usually some of the better-behaved prisoners. Although I never liked him personally, I did come to know quite a bit about Andrei, his family, his hobbies, favorite music. I never thought that he would be capable of such horrible things. I'm not sure if he was motivated by fear from the inmates outside of our doors or by something else while we were distracted with the inmates at our door, but Andrei, who was not fully restrained, started to free the other inmates.

How did you not notice this was going on?

When the prisoners first started their uprising, Indrik was already making his way towards us. Our government was firing on him with what seemed like every missile that we had. Even though we were miles away, every explosion from those missiles could be felt. By the time this was all going on, Indrik had become significantly closer. Each blast shook the prison walls enough to knock us off balance. We used the cameras around the prison to give us a view of the outside. But my guess, Indrik was no more than two miles away. Unfortunately for us, this "minor" distraction almost made us forget entirely about the prisoners. The next thing we knew, Andrei had a blade against Lyndsay's throat and two of the previously restrained prisoners were attacking the guard and I. The other two were nowhere to be seen. Sergei, the guard, was an older man. He could not have been more than a few years from retiring. I remember he would always show us pictures and videos of his grandchildren. He did not deserve to die the way he did.

They killed him?

Almost immediately. They attacked so suddenly that Sergei didn't even have time to draw his weapon. He was shot twice in the struggle, and although he tried his best to defend us, it was just too much for the poor man. After Sergei had been taken care of, the prisoners moved to the door to try and figure out how to open it. Once in lockdown mode, the door could only be opened by select personnel that knew the code. That included myself and Sergei. It was during this initial event that I saw the third prisoner emerge from our critical care room. He was absolutely covered in blood and then it became all too clear why they were here.

They were sent to kill your patient?

I believe so. He was an important enough prisoner that I'm sure he had a significant amount of enemies. My best guess is that they staged the fight to get into the infirmary. The addition of the Kaiju attack was unplanned, but I'm sure worked to their advantage. The third prisoner, Bogdan, was obviously the ringleader. I remember he was very calm but had a way about him that was terrifying. Even if he wasn't covered in someone else's blood, this man was capable of instilling great fear.

What about the fourth inmate?

The big one? He was still restrained in his bed. When these four were brought in, we were told it was for fighting. My best guess is that the three of them attacked the fourth because of his size so that they could all get to the infirmary. They got their wish though, as one inmate received stitches and the other had one of the worst broken noses I had ever seen. Bogdan didn't seem to have any injuries. My guess is that he was the one organizing the fight. The large prisoner had a stab wound in his shoulder and a few cuts but seemed mostly fine. Bogdan barked orders at his dogs, demanding that they get the key to the medicine closet. He then proceeded to threaten me and the nurse and tell us all of the things they would do to us if we didn't comply. I remember thinking that we were dead either way and that I just hoped the Kaiju would step on us before these inmates had their way with us.

How the hell did you get out of this? I'm sorry, but I can't imagine any scenario where this would end up with you sitting here, talking to me today.

Neither could I. Like I said, I was sure that we were going to die. I think the only thing that saved us was, oddly enough, Indrik itself. I remember as Bogdan was issuing his threats, he was called over by his stooge with the broken nose to look at the prison cameras. We had been hearing some commotion beyond the doors, but with all of the excitement, we barely noticed a difference. What Bogdan saw on the camera must have terrified him because as soon as he did, he began asking about ways to escape. There were no ways out of the infirmary, just one door in and one door out, and he was looking at it. He did not like this answer very much, kicking me in the gut upon receiving the bad news. He began to pace around, trying to think of what to do, when he looked over to the big inmate. He seemed to stare at him for a little while, piecing together a plan in his head.

After some thinking, he walked over to the inmate's bed and asked him if he wanted to live. During this entire ordeal, the inmate hadn't said anything. He had just watched on in silence. He looked at Bogdan and nodded his head yes. Bogdan seemed fairly relieved and began to loosen the inmate's restraints. While he was doing this, he was talking about there being no hard feelings and that they weren't going to kill him in that fight, that they just needed to rough him up enough to make it look real. After cutting him loose, Bogdan turned to us and began barking orders again. I am assuming that they were something about escaping and such, but I was distracted when the large inmate stood up behind Bogdan. We knew that he was tall, but when they brought him in, he was strapped to the stretcher. Seeing the seven-footer tower over Bogdan, who is not a small man to begin with, was terrifying. Not nearly as terrifying, though, as when this monster of a man grabbed Bogdan by the head and began to squeeze. Sure, Bogdan was trying to fight back, but it didn't seem to be doing any good as his eyes began to pop out of his skull. His henchmen watched in horror and I think I heard Andrei even threaten to kill Lyndsay if he didn't let go. These threats fell on deaf ears as the monster was focused on his task at hand. I remember Bogdan beginning to scream, but the more he seemed to struggle the tighter the large inmate's grip seemed to get before finally I heard a crunch and then Bogdan's lifeless body fell to the ground. Bogdan's goons watched in horror as the monster their master had just let loose began to walk towards them.

What happened next was a blur of brutality as this monster of a man attacked the remaining inmates like a caged animal. At first, they both tried to overpower him, but that didn't happen. When it was clear they were outmatched, one tried to run away while the other was trapped in the giant's grip. Andrei seemed distracted during this time and we took advantage of that. He still had the blade up to Lyndsay's neck but was watching the horror in front of him, paying little attention to us. I knew that this was the only chance I had to get Lyndsay free. I barreled into Andrei with my entire body, knocking him off balance. Lyndsay then turned to face the man and together, we were able to overpower him and turn the blade on him. I'm not proud of what we did next, but it was either us or him at that point. There was no person in front of me, there was no Hippocratic Oath, there was just me and survival.

After we dealt with Andrei, we turned to face the other prisoners, but there was nothing left of them, nothing except for this new creature that had just been unleashed. We were unsure if he would come for us next. I still had the blade in my hand and prayed that I wouldn't have to use it. There was something different in the prisoner's demeanor, though, something in his eyes. It almost seemed like he didn't even care that we were there with him. He had dealt with Bogdan and his men and was now staring intently at the camera monitors. He was silent for a while, but he did not look happy with what he was seeing. He eventually spoke for the first time, asking me if there was any other way out of here besides this door. I was still in shock somewhat, so all I could do was shake my head no. All he said then was, "Well, we might be in a little bit of trouble then," as he then motioned for us to come look at the cameras. We walked over cautiously, but when I finally looked at the screens, I no longer cared about the monster that was standing in front of me. That's when we saw the creatures on the screen. They had overrun the prison and were ripping the inmates apart.

Creatures? So not Indrik?

No, in fact. During all of the excitement, Indrik seemed to have passed us by. Looking at our outdoor cameras, he seemed to be farther away now. This made sense too, as the facility was shaking much less now.

What did you think these creatures were then? Indrik's offspring?

No, no. Indrik resembled a walking mountain with the face of a rhinoceros. These creatures looked almost bug-like. They were the size of baboons and jumped around like them too. I assume they came from Indrik either way. My best guess is that they were some sort of parasite that had attached itself to the much larger Kaiju. This sort of thing isn't uncommon in nature, but when dealing with such an uncommon creature, it is hard to know for sure. The only thing that was certain was that they were not friendly, and they certainly seemed to enjoy the taste of human flesh.

What was the plan? To stay in the secured area?

That was my plan. Especially after seeing those creatures, I wanted nothing to do with anything outside of those doors. The larger prisoner had other plans, however. He began to ask how to open the doors and which routes were quickest for escaping the prison. At that moment, I had forgotten everything I had just seen this man do. I began yelling at him. I could not fathom why he would want to escape these walls. I kept yelling at him that they would kill us and that he would never be free if we left this room! He stayed very calm throughout this one-sided discussion, but something in his face had changed. It was a calm determination. After I had finished yelling at him, he began to speak.

"We are dead regardless of whichever room we stay in. Those creatures outside are nothing. The real threat is with our military. They have been trying to put that creature down for days now and nothing seems to work. It is only a matter of time before they stop caring about the lives of civilians and only focus on killing this creature. We need to get as far away from this location as we possibly can."

He was right, of course. I couldn't argue with his logic. Indrik had been roaming around the countryside for almost two days now. It was a miracle that the government didn't resort to extreme measures already. The prisoner then grabbed my hand in a type of forced handshake and began to speak to us once more.

"My name is Jamie. I do not plan or wish either of you harm, but make no mistake, Doctor, I am escaping this prison. Whether you choose to help me or stay here is up to you, but do not get in my way."

He was making the same face that he did before he fought with Bogdan and his men, so I knew that he was serious, and although I was still very uneasy about trusting him, I figured it was better for us to travel with him than to wait here.

So you opened the doors?

Not right away. First, we grabbed the guard's gun and a few other items that we could fashion into some weapons. I also had Lyndsay grab a bag of first aid equipment. Whatever happened out there, I wanted us to be ready. Jamie found some riot gear in the guard's station and put it on. He then asked me if we had any stimulants.

Stimulants?

He wanted drugs, although he claimed it wasn't for an addiction. I argued against it for obvious reasons, but his argument was that if he should be attacked, he did not want to be distracted by the pain. I still didn't agree, but it didn't seem like I had much of a choice. To be honest with you, at worst, I figured he would be too coked out of his mind and would distract the creatures while me and Lyndsay escaped. Given his immense size, I injected him a slightly higher than normal dosage. Lyndsay and I then went to open the door and he stood behind us, still getting used to the effects of the drugs. Before opening the door, I asked him how he felt. He opened his eyes, which were now as black as the abyss, and replied, "Like a monster."

What was the plan? Even if you made it out of the prison, then what?

We knew that a few of the buses had still been left behind during the evacuation. All that stood between us and those buses was one long prison hallway and some bloodthirsty monsters. Our plan was to get through the prison, using Jamie as a battering ram for anything in our way, find a bus with the keys still in the ignition, and get as far away from this location as possible.

Once we opened the doors to the rest of the prison, we realized the situation was far worse than we could've imagined. There had to be hundreds of those creatures. At first, they didn't notice the doors opening, they were too preoccupied with eating their fresh kills. The floors were covered with what was left of the prisoners that, just a few minutes ago, were trying so desperately to get in to our wing. For a second, I thought that we might be able to sneak past them, but only for a second. Jamie had other plans as he started to scream and then charge towards the creatures like a charging rhino. We followed close behind, hitting anything that moved in our general direction. We were trying to conserve the bullets if we could, instead using the guard's baton.

The show of force that Jamie exhibited earlier against Bogdan and his men was nothing compared to this drug-fueled aggression that he was now engulfed in. I couldn't tell which noises were coming from the creatures and which were coming from Jamie himself. He was punching, kicking, and even throwing the creatures as he charged down the hallway. He was showing little regard for our safety in the process, and even less for his. When we finally got to the end of the hallway and opened up the doors, it was the first time I had seen any sunlight in the last two days. We ran towards the only bus left in the lot. It was a little dinged up from the creatures, but it looked like it would still drive. We ran onto the bus and shut the door as the creatures followed in after us. Jamie was holding the door shut with all his might, yelling at us to start the bus. Lyndsay was nervously turning the keys in the ignition. I had a pipe that I was using to whack anything that was trying to get in through the windows. Just as we started to hear the rumble of the engine, the back of the bus erupted in a shower of glass as one of the creatures had broken through the backdoor window, with more following. We both yelled for Lyndsay to drive, and she screamed, slamming her foot on the gas and knocking all of us off-balance, including our unwanted passenger. Jamie was the first to his feet, running up to the creature in the backseat, kicking it like a fútbol out the rear door they had broken through. We soon left the creatures behind as we drove out the prison gates. Leaving those walls behind was the first time I had felt truly at ease during this whole ordeal. I truly felt like we were going to make it. Lyndsay was cheering, and Jamie was even smiling. I remember thinking we were going to make it, until suddenly the bus was hit by something from the side, launching it and us into the air. I was knocked off my feet. I hit the side of the bus fairly hard. I had cuts all over my face, arms, and neck, and I was fairly certain my arm was broken. I stayed awake through that whole ordeal, as did Jamie. Lyndsay was not as lucky however. She had serious head trauma during the crash and did not make it.

What hit you? Another vehicle?

From what I can gather, Indrik was able to get a hold of one of the jets that was attacking him and threw it in our general direction. It hit the side of the road and the explosion was enough to knock the bus into the air. So, we were fucked. Jamie and I were able to help each other out of the bus. His leg was torn to shreds, and even with the amount of drugs he was on, the pain was probably excruciating. I myself felt like I could barely breathe, let alone move. The adrenaline was starting to wear off and I was noticing more and more injuries on myself. We weren't going anywhere and just as things seemed like they couldn't get any worse, we began to hear the screeches of the parasite creatures coming towards us. With the creatures to the front of us and Indrik at our back, things seemed very hopeless. Jamie sat me down against the bus and handed me the gun he had taken from the guard, saying, "There are six bullets left. If I don't make it, use this." At first, I didn't understand what he was saying. I thought that we could at least try and hide someplace, but it looked like Jamie's mind was made up. As Jamie stood up, it was clear that he was starting to come down from his high. He began to run, or at least run as fast as he could, towards the approaching swarm of creatures. Jamie screamed throughout his entire charge until he collided with the swarm. He was an absolute terror, fighting until the very end, until the swarm overtook him and I could no longer see him standing amongst the beasts. It wasn't long before one of the creatures began to lose interest in whatever was left of Jamie and started to wander towards me.

Did you try to hide?

I could barely lift the gun that Jamie had just handed me, let alone try and hide. I debated shooting the approaching creature at first, but I was worried it would alert the others. I noticed a couple more stragglers that were wandering towards me from the group. I was hoping that they might lose interest and change direction. I knew as soon as I fired the first shot that the rest of the swarm would come at me. Of course, one of the approaching creatures did eventually notice me, forcing me to fire at it. I hit it right in the shoulder, making it collapse and start to scream in pain. The other creatures began to notice their brethren's wails and soon charged towards me. I shot at the approaching creatures, but I was firing wildly, missing almost all of my shots. Each shot made my arm feel like it was going to fall off. It wasn't until the creature jumped towards me that I finally hit it. Its lifeless corpse still landed on me, making me yell in pain upon impact. The rest of the swarm had been alerted to my presence at this point and was making their way towards me. I remember taking everything in as I held a gun up to my head, trembling. Tears began to roll down my face and I remember thinking if it hadn't been for the present situation, this was actually a very beautiful sunset, and then I pulled the trigger.

You shot yourself?

I tried to, but It seemed that I had used all of the gun's bullets trying to get rid of the creatures. I began to panic, pulling the trigger again and again and again, until finally I heard the gunshot. Only, it wasn't mine. Just as I was about to be overtaken by the swarm, a barrage of bullets began to fall upon the creatures as KRSD operatives emerged from behind the bus. They began firing on the creatures until there was nothing left of the swarm. I yelled for help with every bit of strength I had left. The medics found me and were able to administer first aid. I was evacuated to the nearest KRSD facility, where I told them my story. Instead of sending me back to Russia, they instead offered me a job. Given the experience I had just had, I was in favor of a career change. To this day, I'll never fully understand why Jamie did what he did for me. I'm not sure if he thought he could distract the creatures long enough for me to escape or if he just wanted to go down fighting. I'll never know. What I do know is that I wouldn't be standing here today if not for his actions.

RUN AWAY

SURVIVAL

In the winter of 1982, the small town of Georgetown, located in the Prince Edward Island Province of Canada, faced a Kaiju attack without warning. This Kaiju, now codenamed Wendigo, was a Category II Terra Class that resembled a giant wolf. In the dead of night, Wendigo crept into Georgetown's streets and began her attack. By the time the rest of the townsfolk were aware of Wendigo's presence, she had already decimated almost half the population. Luckily for Georgetown resident Liam Condit and his family, they had an underground shelter that they were able to hide in until the Kaiju was properly dealt with by the military. Unfortunately for the Condit family, the military didn't receive word of the Kaiju until almost three weeks after the attack. Canada faces severe winters even in the mildest of years, but in the year of 1982, Prince Edward Island was facing one of the worst recorded blizzards on record. Whether the blizzard was caused by natural occurrences, the Wendigo, or a combination of the two, the town of Georgetown lost all power during the storm. With the power cut off to the rest of the town, Wendigo continued her reign of terror.

Over the next few days, she fed on poorly hidden survivors and nearby wildlife, but then something strange happened. Usually when a food source runs out, a Kaiju will move on to the next area. Wendigo didn't. When her food supply ran out, she began to search for the survivors held up underground. What we now know is that Wendigo possessed a type of heat vision that allowed her to see a glimpse of where the survivors were. She began to dig and break her way into the basements on many remaining survivors. The people of Georgetown had essentially dug their own graves and were sitting ducks for Wendigo. Most shelters lack a proper escape route that allows their residents to safely exit in case of emergencies.

These underground shelters are not impenetrable. If a Kaiju is made aware of your presence, they will do whatever it takes to get to you. This is why it is important to have more than one escape route. When a Kaiju attacks your shelter, 9 times out of 10, it will come through the entrance. Luckily for the Wilson family, Liam thought ahead on this and was able to evacuate his family safely from their shelter without Wendigo noticing, but their problems weren't over yet. While the Condit family had escaped the wrath of Wendigo, they were still out in the elements with the nearest town almost five miles away. While they did have supplies and proper clothing for the elements, the hazard of the blizzard, as well as the harsh terrain, made it extremely difficult for them. There were four members of the Condit family when they left the shelter. By the time the Condit family was discovered outside the town of Melbourne, only one had survived.

The point of this story is to show that even the most secure locations are still vulnerable to Kaiju attack. When that happens, you and your group will need a secure escape and enough supplies to face the outside elements. Like in the Wendigo attack, help will not always arrive quickly and sometimes, it will be up to you to ensure your loved one's safety. This chapter contains details on survival equipment, transportation, and how to survive different terrain/climates around the world. These tactics come from trained professionals and survivors of some of the worst Kaiju attacks in history.

EQUIPMENT/SUPPLIES

When faced with a hazardous situation requiring evacuation, one should always have a survival kit on hand. These kits are meant to have food and health supplies, as well as a temporary shelter for each member of the group. The shelters within these kits vary depending on the environment but the most common examples are tarps, space blankets, and tube tents. Mostly, when referring to a survival kit, we are talking about a large kit that is transported in a vehicle instead of being carried by an individual. These kits include the temporary shelters discussed above, medical supplies, tools for signaling/navigating, multipurpose tools, and enough water/food for your whole party. This is often different from the smaller bags survivalists recommend having on hand for each individual. These bags are called bug-out bags.

A bug-out bag (BOB) is a bag of supplies that one should have prepared in case of emergencies. These bags are also referred to as quick run bags (QRB), get out of dodge bags (GOOD bag), and personal emergency relocation kits (PERK). Regardless of the name used, this bag contains all supplies, medical equipment, and tools that a person would need to survive for up to 72 hours. While a bug-out bag is similar to a survival kit, they focus more on evacuation rather than long-term survival and are meant to be easily transported in a backpack or small bag. The primary purpose of this bag is to allow you to evacuate quickly should disaster suddenly strike. The 72-hour recommendation comes from emergency responders saying that in a disaster, it could take them up to 72 hours to reach the affected area. Your typical bag should include the following at a minimum:

-**Water:** 4 liters per person per day is recommended, 2 liters for drinking and 2 liters for cleaning. Depending on your area's climate, you can add a liter for drinking each day.

- **Food:** Your food should be nonperishable. Canned goods are a good choice.

- **Water purification tablets/supplies:** When tablets run out, your next option is to boil the water.

- **Cooking supplies/utensils:** It is recommended each party member have their own eating utensils. It is also wise to pack a can opener and basic tools such as a spatula and tongs.

- **Multi-vitamins:** These can be a good supply of nutrients when food runs out

- **Medical supplies:** Unless members of your group have a specific condition such as diabetes, your medical equipment should really only include things you would find in a first aid kit, such as gauze, bandages, sterile gloves, tape, and medical scissors.

- **Appropriate clothing:** Dress appropriately for the climate you are in. In emergency situations, each person is expected to rotate between the clothes they have on and the clothes in your bag. Your bag should have no more than one change of clothes in order to save space. While your outer wear will be worn for extended periods of time, it is recommended that you pack a few pairs of socks and underwear. This will help you maintain good hygiene as well as help protect your feet during travel. Your socks should be changed at least once a day in order to avoid your feet and socks becoming too moist. This foot sweat will not only affect your hygiene, but it could seriously hurt you as well. When your socks get dirty, they cannot breathe. This means your sweat and everything else gets trapped in there. Eventually, the moisture builds up and causes your skin to get soft and wrinkled. If this goes on for too long then your skin will start to peel, resulting in blisters, sores, fungus infections, and in extreme cases, gangrene. Many soldiers know this phenomena by its other name, trench foot. The best way to prevent this is by keeping your feet warm and dry if you're able to.

-**Fire-starting tools:** This can include matches (preferably waterproof), lighters, and even batteries. Whatever will get the job done and is easy to carry.

-**Maps:** Each map should have key locations circled on it, such as hospitals, military bases, and rally points should the rest of the group get separated.

-**Camping equipment:** A sleeping bag and a small tent are ideal.

-**Weather protection:** Hats, gloves, ponchos, goggles, umbrellas, etc.,

- **Bedding items:** Sheets and blankets are good substitutes for sleeping bags. If you have room, you should also pack a small pillow and a tarp. If you're forced to camp overnight, placing a tarp below your tent/bedding will help keep you dry from ground moisture. The tarp could also be fashioned into a makeshift shelter if a tent isn't an option. Tarps are also useful for collecting drinking water when it storms.

- **Any additional medicine:** This is for anyone in the group with special health needs, children, or the elderly. This doesn't have to be for only serious conditions. In fact, it is recommended that you have medicine for headaches and stomach pain.

- **A copy of your medical records**

- **Care needs for pets:** Dishes for food and water, pet food if possible, flea/tick medicine, gear to secure them (collars and leashes, etc.,)

- **At least one knife:** A utility and tactical knife if possible.

- **Duct tape**

- **Rope/Paracord:** You can also use thin wire for hunting and fishing.

- **Photo I.D.**

- **A compass**

- **Cash:** While not completely useless, credit cards won't serve you well if you're trying to purchase items in areas without electricity.

- **Signal mirror**

- **Emergency whistle:** While a whistle could get you some unwanted attention from the Kaiju, this is still a good tool to have should you or others get separated from the group. It is stressed that you should only use your whistle when you are a safe distance away from the monsters.

- **Firearms and ammunition:** This should be an easy to transport firearm that you can maintain easily in the field. Hopefully, the most you will have to use this for is hunting for food or self-defense. In the event of a Kaiju attack, a handgun won't do much.

- **Garbage bags:** These can act as makeshift ponchos, shelters, and many other uses.

- **Super glue:** This can be used to repair items or people. In the event of an emergency, it is not uncommon for people to glue their wounds shut when medical supplies are scarce.

- **Hatchet:** This is useful for cutting down tree limbs for fires, as well as for self-defense. You can also use the back side of the axe head as a makeshift hammer.

- **Pepper spray:** This is good to have on hand should you need to defend yourself from people or animals.

- **Feminine hygiene products: If there are women traveling in the group, their kits should contain these products, such as tampons or pads.**

- **Eye protection:** You will want something durable that will protect your eyes from the elements and debris.

- **Flashlight:** Something that is easy to carry, flashlights can also be used as a signaling tool to others in your group. It is also recommended that you have some glow sticks that you can use in order to save the flashlight's battery life.

- **Emergency literature:** These books (like this one) should be studied well before any actual emergency takes place and should only need to be used as a reference. It is recommended that you put tabs into these books for parts that you think will be important. Books that detail emergency medical practices or natural disasters are some examples.

TRANSPORTATION

Finding reliable transportation during any disaster is difficult, let alone when that disaster is a 100-foot-tall rampaging monster looking for a snack. Even if you have a reliable vehicle, it could still be useless due to area congestion. During emergencies, everyone in the area will more than likely be attempting to evacuate. This can create traffic jams and ultimately stop you and your loved ones from escaping. It only takes one bad accident or vehicle breaking down on a main route to prevent escape. There is also the possibility that the route has been destroyed. Every step the Kaiju take causes destruction. Bridges, roads, even underground tunnels all face the possibility of being destroyed.

There is also the likelihood of these escape routes being blocked by some sort of debris, from the monster or otherwise. This isn't to say all automobiles are useless, in fact, quite the contrary. Your vehicle of choice may be the only thing that keeps you alive in a Kaiju attack. For that reason, we will go over some basic types of transportation and their usefulness. Like other sections of this guide, we will not go into great detail for every type of automobile. We will only go over the basics, arming you with simple facts to give you a foundation for survival.

PRIMARY VEHICLES

These are the more common vehicles that people use for travel. While we cannot possibly look at every available vehicle, we will still discuss the pros and cons of the most common automobiles available to civilians. Key things to look for should be gas mileage, available space, off-road capabilities, and safety.

I. SEDAN/HATCHBACK

One of the most common cars driven around the world, a sedan is often considered the basic car. These vehicles are built low to the ground, allowing for easier maneuverability in urban areas. Capable of carrying up to five people, this is a decent enough choice if you live in the city, but bad if the need might arise for off-road travel. Sedans are not typically built for large trunk space, meaning you may have to limit the amount of supplies you carry. This is where a hatchback would be more useful. A hatchback is a sedan, only with larger trunk space, making it ideal if you need to transport more supplies than the typical sedan can hold. This large trunk space however typically means that there is less room for passengers. Many newer model sedans are now built with an abundance of safety and travel features, including four-wheel drive. While this is a step in the right direction, if there is any chance you will be traveling outside of city streets or main highways, then a sedan may not be the best vehicle for you.

2. SUV

On paper, the SUV should be the optimal choice for travel during any disaster. This large, rugged vehicle is capable of carrying a large amount of passengers/supplies, it's built for all-terrain travel, and focuses on safety.

Unfortunately, not all of these features are actually included in most SUV models. Not all SUVs are capable of all-terrain driving. In fact, many of them are built for city and residential areas, much like the sedan. This could be a nightmare should someone not do their research and expect their SUV to perform off road.

Safety is another feature that SUVs face criticism on, with past models not meeting the safety standards promised and performing below average in tests. Since 2009 however, most SUV models have consistently performed better in these tests, with some even being named amongst the safest vehicles on the market.

Size is the one thing, however, that all SUVs have a great deal of, with the smallest models being able fit the same number of passengers as a large sedan. These vehicles can be a good choice for travel during a Kaiju attack, but you should do your research carefully when selecting a model. While the SUVs have made improvements over the years, that doesn't mean the newest models are reliable. Do your research and choose carefully.

3. VAN

Vans can be a good travel option for large families living in a residential area. They have significant space and their low ground clearance makes getting passengers in and out easier than with an SUV. In a Kaiju attack, however, you will have to search far and wide to find a worse death trap then a van. Vans are not made for maneuverability, making escape difficult for its driver. Also, most vans do not possess all-wheel drive, making them only dependable for city and residential driving. While different models have increased safety features while on the road, during a Kaiju attack, the only thing a van can be relied on is for serving the Kaiju with canned food.

4. JEEP

Considered the ultimate all-terrain vehicle by many outdoor enthusiasts, jeeps are built to travel where most vehicles cannot. Most jeeps are built with four-wheel drive and can be modified so their performance better matches the needs of different terrain. While good for traveling through most fields/trails, jeeps are not the best choice in colder climates. Jeeps are not known for being the most spacious vehicles, with many only being able to fit up to four people. This lack of space will also affect the amount of supplies you can travel with. Add that with the typically low gas mileage and a jeep may not be your best choice of travel. If you live in a warmer area and have no more than two people in your party, then a jeep isn't a bad choice for a quick escape. If you are a family of four needing to escape and travel a large distance then perhaps you should rethink your travel options.

5. TRUCK

A truck, much like a van, presents many obstacles for safe travel. Many will cite a truck's durability, off-road capability, and power as prime reasons they are a great travel choice. The reality is that most trucks are bulky, clunky, have poor gas mileage, and can be very loud. Any one of these things would make this vehicle a poor choice for escaping the Kaiju. If, however, you want a vehicle that will draw the monster's attention, then look no further than a large diesel truck.

A truck's main selling point is that it is powerful and it allows the driver to transport cargo. While those are useful traits in everyday life, it is not so useful when the monsters come. Anything you should need (not want) to transport should be able to fit in the trunk of a sedan. The other benefit many will cite is a truck's off-road capability. While it is true that trucks are typically better for off-road travel than most cars, few are able to dependably perform the way television commercials make them seem. KRSD cleanup crews have found the wreckage of many trucks with some parts of their passengers still inside. It is believed that many of these civilians thought they could escape the Kaiju by driving off-road, only to have their truck get stuck in the mud. The Kaiju are thankful for this snack, but the passengers not so much.

6. BUS/RV

I have already used the canned food reference when speaking about the van, but that reference also fits perfectly when speaking of buses or RVs. These driving death traps are large, loud, and slow. These vehicles have no off-road capabilities, low fuel capabilities, and next to no maneuverability. The only thing that is beneficial about these vehicles is their ability to carry many passengers/resources. Unfortunately, this typically doesn't matter when the monsters attack. Due to the Kaiju's heightened senses, they are able to find food sources easily. Those foolish enough to hide in a bus are typically the first of many victims in a Kaiju's feeding frenzy.

7. ARMORED CAR

While it is unlikely that civilians will have access to armored vehicles, it is not unheard of. Due to a person's job or wealth, they may have such access and choose to use it. An armored vehicle wouldn't be your worst choice during a Kaiju attack, but it also wouldn't be your best. These vehicles aren't made with off-roading or gas mileage in mind. Additionally, they aren't really made for safety either. What they are really meant for is transporting valuable items and keeping those items secure and inside the vehicle. The driver/passengers are an afterthought. While armored vehicles may stop bullets, they would do little against a Kaiju. Even if the monsters couldn't penetrate the armor, they can still throw it. A Kaiju doesn't have to break through to hurt you. They just have to hurt the shell you're hiding in.

8. MOTORCYCLE

This section discusses dirt bikes, motorcycles, and scooters. Dirt bikes are easily the best escape vehicle for someone that needs to make a fast exit. While not ideal for families, these could be very useful for an individual. These cycles are maneuverable and can be driven off-road. What they lack in gas and safety, they more than make up for in practicality. Unlike all of the vehicles listed so far, a cycle is able to weave in-between traffic, making it useful during traffic jams. While motorcycles are just as useful in urban areas, their lack of off-road capability makes the dirt bike a prime choice.

Scooters, unlike motor cycles and dirt bikes, should be avoided. These machines can be clunky, slow, and lack off-road capability. Cycles do face some drawbacks though, gas being one of the biggest. If you do run out of gas, however, a motorcycle is usually light enough for you to push along to the nearest fuel station. Safety can be an issue as well, with no straps or safety belts to protect the riders, they face the danger of being thrown from the bike on impact. Noise is another concern, with most cycles being quite loud (like any other vehicle) when speeding. This could easily attract some unwanted attention from people and Kaiju alike. With all of that being said, most single riders still prefer their bikes over a traditional vehicle.

9. SNOWMOBILE

Take everything discussed about motorcycles, replace the terrain with snow and ice, and you have a snowmobile. These snow machines are incredibly useful in harsh winter climates. They can go off road, up hills, and even over ice, making them a must-have for someone who lives in colder climates. The biggest drawback to these vehicles can be the upkeep. Snowmobiles are a hobby vehicle, and due to the harsh climate they are used in, must be properly maintained. Similar to the motorcycles, snowmobiles are good for a quick escape and all-terrain travel but lack sufficient room for supplies. If driving any of these smaller vehicles, you should take extra care in preparing your bug-out bag and supplies for a quick escape. Remember that what seems like a small Kaiju attack can quickly escalate to an all-out catastrophe that will force you to ration what little supplies you have on hand.

10. VEHICLE MAINTENANCE EQUIPMENT

Along with a bug-out bag and supplies, each vehicle should come with tools for maintenance and repair. The following tools should be kept on hand:

- **Instruction manual**
  - **Tire repair kit**
  - **Air pump**
  - **Gas canisters (For fuel storage)**
  - **Jumper cables**

- Tire jack
- Tools (wrenches, screw drivers, etc.,)
- Replacement parts (wiper blades, tires, etc.,)
- A towel (to clean yourself/ your equipment after making repairs)

ALTERNATE TRANSPOTATION

In the event your primary vehicle fails or becomes unusable, these alternate vehicles may be your only means of land travel.

1. HORSE

The original all-terrain vehicle, horses have been ideal transport for mankind as far back as 2000 BCE. Horses have many of the benefits of the vehicles listed above with almost none of the drawbacks. While cars require fuel and an understanding of automotive maintenance, horses only require food and water, the same as a human, and some basic care. These animals can traverse the most difficult terrain, whether there is a path or not, at speeds of some cars.

Unlike cars, that require only a basic knowledge to operate, a horse requires the understanding of its rider before it can be useful. Horses aren't machines that you can command, they are animals that require skill to ride. No random person off the street can jump on the back of a horse and expect great success. It is highly advised you seek out proper training before attempting to ride a horse, otherwise you are likely to get seriously hurt in your escape.

Horses can be easily spooked, and in a Kaiju attack, you will be lucky to find one. Like any other animal, horses seem to sense when a Kaiju is near and will attempt to flee if they sense this danger. It is advised to be extra cautious around these animals during an attack and to pay close attention to their behavior when out in the open. A skittish horse could indicate that a Kaiju or other predator is nearby.

2. BIKE

Easier to maintain then a motorcycle, and much quieter too, a bicycle can prove useful when attempting to escape. If any damage happens to the bike, then they are relatively easy to fix and can be carried if need be. Most bikes are built to be ridden on or off the road as well, so you are only limited by your level of physical fitness when it comes to biking. The biggest drawback you will face from a bike is their lack of speed. A Kaiju is able to outrun most cars, so a bicycle won't do much good if you're spotted by these monsters.

CIVILIAN AIRCRAFT

The one road that never runs out of room is the wild blue yonder. Air travel is arguably the most expeditious form of escape when the monsters come. It should be noted that this section deals mainly with Aquatic and Terra Class Kaiju. An Aero Class is capable of doing great damage to even the most equipped aircraft. If there is a Kaiju in the sky, stay hidden and stay as low to the ground as possible.

1. HELICOPTER

While they can be quite loud and slow, a helicopter has many advantages over fixed-wing aircraft that makes it a valuable option during an attack. Helicopters can land and take off from virtually any flat surface. Unlike fixed-wing aircraft that need a runway for arrivals or departures, helicopters can land anywhere they can safely put the gear down. This means they face less danger if they run out of fuel as they won't need to worry about making it to an airfield. They just land wherever they need to.

2. FIXED-WING

A fixed-wing aircraft is what most people think about when they think of air travel. A person with access to and knowledge of how to fly a plane may be the safest person on the planet during a Kaiju attack. These aircraft are faster than almost all other forms of travel and are capable of taking their passengers great distances, fuel permitting. Fixed-wing aircraft can typically hold more people and supplies than a helicopter, which makes them a favorite for Kaiju survivalists. The biggest drawback to these aircraft is fuel. While the amount of fuel they can hold varies with each aircraft type, its passengers will literally live or die by how much fuel is in the plane. Planes need a runway for safe takeoff and landing, and these runways may be few and far between depending on the area. This can create a problem if you're 1000 feet in the air and running low on fuel. While some planes are made for water landings/takeoffs, the amount of Kaiju and other predators in the sea might make you rethink that option.

3. AIR BALLOON

Believe it or not, some civilians have attempted to escape the Kaiju using air balloons, but not with much success. Most land-based Kaiju cannot reach helicopters or planes due to their altitude and maneuverability. An air balloon is slow, remains relatively close to the ground, and is hard to maneuver for even an experienced pilot. These aircraft depend too much of the environment for the pilot to effectively control the balloon at all times. It is an obscure option for a reason and can lead to nothing more than an air-delivered meal straight to the Kaiju's mouth.

TERRAIN TRAVEL

Sometimes, things don't go according to plan. Even when you have taken all the necessary steps to survive the Kaiju, it still may not be enough. You could be forced out of your shelter or vehicle and need to evade the monsters. In this worst-case scenario, you and your loved ones will be out in the open and exposed to the effects of nature. This section details the different types of terrain you could be forced to travel through. We will discuss the dangers associated with each terrain, details on building a shelter, as well as some must-have resources for survival. There are many other texts, videos, or instructional guides on surviving each individual climate and it is suggested you seek them out. This section will offer only a general overview of each potential terrain.

1. FORESTS

When discussing forests, we are talking about the kind typically found closer to the northern hemisphere. These temperate locations are full of life and offer a multitude of ways for a skilled outdoorsman to survive. Forests are typically further inland and surrounded by hilly terrain. They possess many trees and other types of natural camouflage for survivors to hide in. On top of that, this terrain is usually full of different types of plants and animals that can be used for resources. In many ways, a forest is the ideal terrain if you need to escape a Kaiju attack, but it does come with some drawbacks.

Forests can be tricky to navigate at times and if you are an inexperienced outdoorsman, it is easy to get lost. While there are many plants that can be eaten or used for medicine, there are also plants that can be poisonous and even deadly to humans. Another thing to remember is that man is not the only predator in the forest. Most of these areas are thriving ecosystems full of all manner of beasts. A bear or pack of wolves can be just as deadly as a Kaiju, and you are in their domain.

The biggest threat one will face in this terrain, however, is other humans. When the Kaiju come, many people will be in a panic and will escape to wherever they think is safest. That usually means out of the cities and into the country, and what better place is there to go then a forest full of nature's gifts? While this thought is true for a small group of survivors, a large group may create problems. People can do terrible things to survive. Most people aren't bad people, but if given the choice between your survival and theirs, odds are they will pick their own.

Be sure to dress appropriately for the time of year and your climate. It is also a good idea to learn about local wildlife and have manuals on hand for identifying harmful/helpful plants.

2. TROPICS

Tropical regions, such as jungles, are thriving ecosystems full of all types of plants and animals. These areas are typically more humid then the average northern forests and can face dangerous heatwaves. Heavy rainfall and storms can hit out of nowhere and should be taken into account when picking a campsite. This climate is usually close to a seashore or water source of some kind and can be a preferable area for a Kaiju to settle on land.

Kaiju aren't the only creatures that appreciate this climate though, with germs, bacteria, and bugs all thriving here. Snakes and other reptiles can often be found in these areas, enjoying the humidity and abundant plant life. Tropical jungles can have much of the same benefits of forests with their vast plant and wildlife. These areas are full of resources. Much like forests though, it is easy for someone to get hurt or killed in the jungle. Traversing this terrain can be difficult, with much of it changing from jungle brush to swamplands. One should have a machete on them at all times for cutting through brush. Use extra caution when traveling through swamp marshes, as they are home to all sorts of dangers (including Kaiju). Watch for bubbles in the water, because those can indicate a possible predator underwater. While Kaiju love this climate, they typically spend most their time in areas of the jungle with a clearing so they can navigate easier. Stay hidden in the bush and use this to your advantage.

3. PLAINS

Plains are wide open terrain with little to no cover other than some simple vegetation, like bushes. Traveling through the plains can be incredibly dangerous with this lack of concealment. A Kaiju could easily spot you from miles away and get to you before you have a chance to hide. You should avoid traveling in such an open area unless it is an absolute necessity. If traveling through this this terrain, be sure to wear clothing or gear that will help you camouflage yourself from the Kaiju. You should also have some scent repellent to avoid being detected from far away. Most importantly, if a Kaiju gets close to you while you are camouflaged, make sure you stay perfectly still and make as little noise as possible. Wait for it to pass by, then continue on your way.

4. FIELDS

Fields, unlike plains, can be beneficial to your group if used correctly. This terrain is very common in farmland and usually covers a wide area. Use the concealment of crops to your advantage when traveling, taking great care to move with stealth. A field can keep you concealed, but it won't make you invisible from the Kaiju. Most fields, depending on the crop, will only grow to be a few feet high. This means that if you are hiding from someone of normal height, then a field might keep you hidden. Against a 50 feet tall monster, however, this is not the case. If someone is making noise and knocking over every stalk as they move, then it is safe to assume a Kaiju will find them. Be sure to use discretion while traveling the fields and avoid drawing much attention to yourself. As stated in the plains section, you should travel in camouflaged clothing and use scent killer while doing so. Never make camp in a field and avoid drawing attention to yourself at all costs.

5. POLAR

Polar environments can be one of the harshest for humans to live in. With below freezing temperatures, blizzards, and a lack of resources, this region can kill you in many different ways, so why is it being discussed as an alternative? Simply because most Kaiju seem to avoid the cold at all cost. While no two Kaiju are exactly the same, many of them share the same biological attributes. The majority of Kaiju spend most of their time in the water. When and if they do come onto land, they mostly enjoy warmer tropical climates. It is rare that Kaiju venture far from the coast before they go back into the water or the military takes them out. For these reasons, mankind has started to embrace living in the cold. While not entirely Kaiju-free, it is unlikely the beasts will make their way up that far before falling to the elements themselves. The danger of freezing is very real in these climates, and in polar climates specifically, your exposed skin can freeze in minutes. Anyone traveling in a polar/tundra region (anywhere cold) should dress appropriately. This means warm clothes, waterproof boots, and goggles (to protect your eyes from snow blindness). Your shelter should be away from areas at a risk for avalanches. Even in the cold, you still need to drink at least one liter of water a day. You can do this by eating snow in the winter and boiled pond water in the summer. Never eat ice, as it can severely hurt you both inside and out. If you are unable to find any animals or fish to eat, it is recommended you find lichens and moss. If able, you want to build your shelter within safe walking distance to a river so that you are able to hunt, scavenge, and better navigate.

Compasses are useless in polar regions. This means that you will need to rely on constellations and shadows to help your navigate. The terrain is constantly changing here, so do not rely on mountains or icebergs as landmarks. If the worst should happen and you fall through the ice, you will want to react violently. Ice water will knock the wind out of you and make you lose consciousness in a matter of minutes. It is important to your survival that you escape the icy cold as quickly as possible. If you should encounter a Kaiju in this area, attempt to camouflage yourself with your surroundings and hide under the snow. Hopefully, this will make the monster lose interest and continue on its way.

6. MOUNTAINS/HILLS

Much like the polar regions discussed above, mountain peaks offer little refuge for humans or Kaiju alike. Many are attracted to the idea of living on top of a mountain and being able to see danger coming from them at all sides. While this is a benefit to living in such a terrain, many fail to develop an escape plan for when that danger comes to their doorstep. Mountains are tricky. While you will be safe from danger in many ways, you are also very isolated, which can be dangerous, especially if you need to make a quick escape.

Most mountain roads, if they have roads, are poorly maintained and can easily fall victim to the effects of nature—snow, ice, falling rocks—so it is strongly advised that if you are planning on settling or traversing mountain terrain that you have proper climbing gear. If climbing as a group, it is important to stay together and work as a team. You should only climb during the day time, as nighttime travel can be too dangerous. When sleeping on the cliffs, you should be safely harnessed and sleep with your head uphill. It is important to cover yourself in some way as the terrain, temperature, and even some wildlife could be harmful. If you should find yourself stranded on a high cliff, you need to seriously weigh your choices, because attempting to climb down may be more dangerous than waiting for rescue.

As a rule, if you are thinking of using mountainous terrain for your escape then you should have proper climbing gear and be familiar with knots and the terrain. Kaiju, like humans, will usually avoid the mountains, preferring to go around it instead of over it unless they are the rare breed that can go through it. In fact, the only Kaiju that have been known to dwell in the mountains have been those capable of flight. Aero Class Kaiju are typically very territorial, so if they do dwell in the mountains near your home, you will surely know.

Hills are a little different from mountain terrain as they are typically not as elevated and are much easier to traverse. On the run, many survivors will run towards hilly terrain in an attempt to get a better view of the surrounding area. While this can be beneficial, the hilly terrain will limit your view until you get to the high point. This means that, depending on the height of the hill, a Kaiju could be right over the other side and you wouldn't know it until it's too late.

7. DESERT

Deserts are some of the harshest climates for humans to survive in. The lack of water and resources mixed with the dramatic changes in temperature make survival difficult for anyone, and that is without adding the possibility of a Kaiju. Kaiju enjoy warmer climates, and it is not uncommon for them to be spotted wandering the deserts of Africa. With little to no cover and such harsh conditions, it is not advised to travel in such climate if you can avoid it. If you cannot avoid it, then at the very least be prepared.

Water is going to be your biggest resource. It is important that you carry enough of it and ration out what you have. If you should run out of water and have no wells on your route, then you only have a few options. If you should come up to a dried spring, you can attempt to dig for water at this location. Sometimes water stays below ground even after a water source has dissipated. The only downside is that the remaining water is usually deep in the earth. You should not overexert yourself trying to get to this water because that can dehydrate you even faster. The other option is for you to exploit water from any plants or cactus you find, depending on your region. These plants usually have water stored up in their roots, which can be extracted. Extraction techniques can vary by plant type, so it is important for you to research the plant life in your surrounding area.

Most desert illness is caused by overexposure to the sun. This means that one needs to be properly clothed and have some sort of shelter (makeshift or otherwise) that is easy to assemble and carry. When building a daytime shelter, it is important to have protection from the intense heat and sunlight. This can be helped by digging into the sand/dirt where the ground is cooler and setting up a sheet/tarp so that it creates a shaded area. Nighttime shelter is a bit more complicated, with some deserts reaching freezing temperatures. To survive this extreme temperature change, you will first want to attempt to build a fire using dry sticks and whatever plants/scrub you can find. You can also use fire to attempt a rescue signal, but be warned that it may attract the Kaiju to your location.

You will want to build a small makeshift wall to protect yourself from wind at night. This wall can be made using rocks from the surrounding area. You will want to use your blanket/tarp to wrap yourself in at night. If you can build a strong enough fire and acquire enough rocks, you can use the fire to heat the rocks so they can help with keeping you warm. Make sure that your clothing is loose fitting and protects your skin from exposure to the sun. This means wearing long flowing garments that are breathable. You will want head and foot protection as well.

Desert terrain is some of the deadliest and should be avoided at all costs.

9. SEASHORE

In most survival guides, a seashore would be some of the best terrain you could hope for. Whether it's a sandy beach or a shore filled with mud and rocks, these areas possess an abundance of food and resources that make survival easier than most climates. Unfortunately for us, the Kaiju also seem to be aware of these benefits. Second only to the ocean, seashores, beaches, and the areas surrounding them face the most Kaiju activity with nine out of ten land-based Kaiju attacks originating from a large body of water. This makes the majority of cities, towns, and islands high risk for a Kaiju attack, and while this is closely monitored, it is something that each area's residents must be prepared for.

In order to better prepare for a Kaiju emergence, it is important to watch for warning signs associated with the Kaiju. For coastal areas specifically, you need to watch for unexplained weather phenomena and the tides. Tides can vary consistently depending on the location and time of year, but an unusual change in the tides can be a warning for Kaiju. When a Kaiju emerges from the ocean, its immense size will often produce some amount of flooding. While the degree of flooding can vary due to the size of the Kaiju, it still poses a direct threat to those near the shore. Look for the warning signs and have an escape plan. If you live near the coast, then try to get as far inland as possible. If you live on an island, then attempt to get off the island so you do not become isolated. If you are able, it is highly recommended that you evacuate by air over sea. Driving is also an option, but your main goal should be escaping the island as quickly and safely as possible.

10. OCEAN

The ocean is a dangerous area to travel in the best of conditions. With harsh weather, dangerous tidal waves, a lack of resources, and all manner of aquatic predators, the ocean is a very dangerous place. Add Kaiju to the mix and it becomes the most dangerous place on Earth. 90% of Kaiju originate from the ocean. Whether this is due to nuclear testing from the past or some paranormal mysticism, scientists at the KRSD aren't sure. What they are sure of is that the ocean is a very dangerous place. The emergence of these monsters over the years has led to some drastic changes in the way the world exports goods, with many cargo ships now having some sort of military or private escort. This has also led to increased numbers in the world's navies, with the U.S. Navy alone almost quadrupling in size over the last 30 years.

URBAN AREAS

This section refers to urban terrain such as cities or residential areas. As a rule of thumb, you should avoid these areas at all costs during a Kaiju attack. This terrain could be a death trap due to the amount of people in a given area. The inspiring skyscrapers of yesterday could easily be turned into today's crushing defeat. Living in a highly populated area presents more dangers then this guide has time to list, but suffice it to say that being in these locations during a Kaiju event will drop your chances of survival by at least 60%. It is easy to get trapped in these areas given how easily traffic jams and crowds can block your escape routes.

This section will detail what to do if you should find yourself trapped in a major city or other populated area. Remember that Kaiju can smell humans, and they will often attack the location with the most food, in this case, wherever the most people are located. It is also important to realize the danger you could face from other survivors. Looting and riots are common in any disaster. It is one thing when you are in a vast forest surrounded by nature and resources; it is a completely different thing when surrounded by people in closer conditions with limited resources. This isn't like being out in the field where you expect (and are hopefully prepared for) no resources. The majority of survivors you meet have in all likelihood never even been outside the city—at least not if it's a major one. These people will be afraid and vulnerable and that can lead to some bad things.

1. SKYSCRAPERS

Skyscrapers (or other high-rise buildings) are common throughout any developed area. These buildings can be a marvel to look at in the best of times, but during a Kaiju attack, they are the last structure you want to be in. No one really knows what draws these monsters to the tallest structures. Whether it is their unquenchable lust for destruction or that they just like climbing on things, most Kaiju are fixated on them. They will either knock over, throw, thrash, crush, or climb on these buildings and everyone inside of them as well. Regardless of how they destroy these manmade monuments, it is important that you are far away from multilevel buildings when the Kaiju attack.

2. SCHOOLS

Schools are a tricky subject, because of the different layouts of each area. No two schools are built the same and depending on the area, they are not built to withstand any sort of catastrophe, especially a rampaging Kaiju. Some schools, such as inner-city schools, are made to withstand some punishment, but this is mostly to protect the students from riots or other such emergencies. If you find yourself needing shelter, you could do much worse than a school building. A school could be a good place to find resources, such as food and basic first aid equipment. Depending on the school, you may be able to find radio equipment that could help your party communicate with rescue teams.

3. HOSPITALS

A hospital could be one of the worst locations to flee to when the monsters come. On paper, hospitals seem great, with vast stores of medical supplies, food, and convenient access to emergency care, so what's the problem? Firstly, hospitals are full of people, most of whom are not capable of caring for themselves. Kaiju have a keen sense of smell for humans in general, but if you throw in the smell of blood, then you are practically ringing the dinner bell. Mix that with a multilevel building of mostly helpless people and you have a situation with no good outcome. After a Kaiju attack, a hospital (or what's left of it) can be a great choice for gathering resources and medical supplies, but never during. If you find yourself trapped in a hospital with a Kaiju approaching, you need to calmly exit the hospital and get to a less-crowded location immediately.

4. POLICE STATIONS

Police stations can have all of the danger of a hospital, with almost none of the benefits. When a Kaiju is reported inbound for an area, most police stations are empty, as the brave men and women on patrol are assisting in evacuations or crowd control efforts. What is left in the police stations is usually an abundance of ammunition, some medical supplies, and whatever essential personnel are left to guard/manage the station. The biggest danger posed by this location isn't the Kaiju, but the people themselves. Whether it is the officers on guard or the panicked looters, whoever is held up at the station will most likely be well armed. While it may seem like a good idea to go to the police station for some ammunition, odds are a lot of other people have had your idea as well. In any emergency, most people will swarm to public safety buildings such as hospitals, police stations, and fire departments. Unfortunately, these buildings can create more chaos in an already chaotic situation.

5. STORES, MARKETS, AND MALLS

This section covers a wide variety of stores, but whether it is a grocery store or a large shopping mall, these areas can have a great amount of resources. With that being said, the general rule of thumb is that the bigger the store is, the more dangerous it will be. For example, most shopping malls are meant to get people in the door, not keep them out. Factor that in with the wide maze of outlet stores inside and you face the danger of being trapped in the store during the chaos of a Kaiju attack. While still not ideal, the smaller stores can offer better protection from Kaiju and small groups of people. In more developed areas, it is common for stores to have roll-down gates, Plexiglas, and even bars on the windows. Obviously, that isn't enough to keep out most Kaiju, but it will do the trick against most people. As long as your group keeps quiet, any passing Kaiju should move on to bigger and louder things.

6. CHURCHES

It is common for people to turn to houses of worship during a state of emergency. While this can be a great benefit to someone spiritually, a church isn't the best place to hide from the Kaiju. Churches offer little in the way security and resources. Churches aren't the worst place to hide out during an attack, but they will not be able to sustain a large group for long.

7. WAREHOUSES

A warehouse can seem like an attractive refuge for some. Most warehouses are spacious, with significant security for protecting the merchandise inside. They also typically have running water and plumbing, something that will be invaluable in an emergency. Those features, combined with the possibility of valuable supplies within the warehouse, make this a good option for most emergencies. Unfortunately, warehouses do come with their share of drawbacks. For starters, many warehouses are near the water, which puts them at high risk for Kaiju attacks. While most warehouses have adequate defenses with barbed wire fences and security locks, none of these will stop a Kaiju. Warehouses can be a good sanctuary, but use extreme caution if using one.

8. PIERS/DOCKS/SHIPYARDS

Due to the lack of cover and the fact that 90% of Kaiju attacks start in or near water, you should avoid these areas at all costs. Any area near water is at a higher risk for Kaiju attacks. When they emerge, they usually bring tidal waves and other storm-like effects that can be felt for miles. Anyone living or working near these areas are taking a huge risk and will often not survive the Kaiju's initial emergence from the sea. Some people will think themselves clever and head towards the sea after the Kaiju has made their way inland, thinking that the Kaiju will not backtrack, but this has proven to be false on multiple occasions. When attacked, Kaiju are like any other animal concerned with its survival. These creatures face a fight or flight dilemma just like the rest of us. When met with heavy resistance, it is not uncommon for a Kaiju to retreat the same way that it came, doing more damage to everything in the process and foiling the would-be haven of the docks.

9. SUBWAYS/UNDERGROUND

Underground locations such as subways or other transit systems are a bit of a double-edged sword. On the one hand, these areas can offer significant protection from the Kaiju. These underground areas are well fortified and have a direct route of escape in the train systems. Their drawbacks, although few, could be devastating. If the power goes out throughout the city, then these trains won't function. This will lead to people overcrowding the underground stations, which are already limited on space, and overcrowding could catch the attention of the passing Kaiju. If the Kaiju should find these underground tunnels, then everyone inside would be at their mercy.

10. BANKS

Banks are one of the worst places to be in a Kaiju attack. Most people think that the security a bank offers would make them a good choice for hiding from the Kaiju. Sadly, this is not the case. Many banks have mediocre security features at best and even those are only designed to defend against bank robbers, not giant monsters. Others think a bank vault would offer them enough security. Yes, most bank vaults are capable of withstanding incredible force, however, they will not offer you any safety. Vaults are meant to keep assets safe, not people. If someone were to lock themselves in a vault, they would be without food or water, and worse, would be running out of air. The other obvious dangers banks face are looters. During an emergency, most people try to get to safety. Other people will see this as an opportunity to steal, and what location has the most stuff worth stealing? You can argue that the bank will most likely be locked down, but the reality is that these are not the smartest people, and when dumb, excited people are trying to steal, they are very dangerous. So, do yourself a favor and just avoid the banks all together.

11. CAPITAL/CITY HALLS

Government buildings have all the danger that a police station or hospital would face, with none of the rewards. These buildings are typically not well fortified and do not possess any valuables. Avoid these and other public buildings with major foot traffic as they will be chaotic during a Kaiju attack.

12. PRISONS

Prisons are not often thought of as a safe haven during emergencies, and for good reason. Prison walls are filled with some of the most dangerous humans on the planet who, even in a monster attack, cannot be trusted. Any prison full of inmates should be avoided at all costs. Though the prison walls may give you a sense of security, the reality is that a prison is only as safe as its fences, camera systems, and the guards patrolling them. None of these things are much of a defense against a Kaiju. Prisons, like any overpopulated area, are at risk of attracting the attention of the Kaiju. While it isn't uncommon for prisons to be evacuated during hurricanes or other natural disasters, it is unlikely to happen when the monsters come. A Kaiju attack is usually very fast and can be over within minutes. While there are some warning signs, the reality is that none of this is enough time to organize an evacuation of thousands of inmates. Should you come across an abandoned prison, it is highly encouraged you make refuge there. Most prisons have an abundance of food, medical supplies, and other resources. While their security may not do much against the Kaiju, they are still better than being out in the open. As long as there aren't too many survivors to attract the attention of the Kaiju, your group should be safe.

13. MILITARY BASES

Military bases are quite possibly the greatest refuge one could hope for during a Kaiju attack. These bases are well fortified, with most of them having primary, secondary, and tertiary defenses that will ensure the safety of every man, woman, and child within their walls. Additionally, these bases are usually full of an abundance of resources, including food, water stores, and even gardens. Perhaps no resource is as valuable, however, as the brave men and women behind these defenses, who are capable of taking the fight to the Kaiju menace by using some of the most advanced weapons the world has ever seen. Many bases have nuclear fallout shelters that are capable of functioning even in the most extreme of emergencies. This makes a military compound a desirable location for any and all nearby survivors. The good news is that due to the needs of the military, most of these bases are in rural, less-populated areas. The bad news is, of course, that many people will be attempting to get into the base from all over the country. While the base has a vast amount of resources, they are limited, and what they have will more than likely be given to our soldiers and their dependents over other survivors. Still, if you are able to get onto a base of any kind before an attack, it is strongly encouraged.

INSECTOIDS

Salt Lake City, Utah

I am greeted at the door by Mrs. Meredith Abrams. Mrs. Abrams is the only survivor of the attack in Arizona. What makes the Arizona attack unique is that it was the first known Kaiju attack to take place on American soil. This is the attack that most of my peers at the KRSD recognize as the beginning of the modern Kaiju era. Meredith has been interviewed countless times her entire life about this incident so there isn't any new information I hope to get from her. I just wanted to record her firsthand account for the KRSD's personal archive. Meredith takes me out to the backyard where her grandchildren are playing. I am offered some lemonade and delicious sandwiches that only a grandmother would know how to make. Looking at her happy demeanor, I would never have guessed this woman had been through such a tragic event.

It was the summer of 1954 when me and my family took our annual camping trip to Arizona. We were Mormon, you see, and out of all the exotic locations they could have sent my father for his missionary work, they sent him to Arizona for two years. [laughs] I think he was hoping for someplace like Asia or Europe, but eventually, he fell in love with the desert. He met my mother during this time. She converted, then after they were married, moved back to Utah. They eventually gave birth to my brother and then me a couple of years later. Dad continued to work in the church and Mom was a home-maker. I guess you could say that we were poor growing up, but us kids would have never known that. Anytime not spent at school or church was spent playing outside or reading stories. We didn't have a lot growing up, but what we did have was worth it. Our parents would constantly take us camping because it was all we could afford to do. Just to drive around and explore, which to a kid is the best type of fun. At least once a year, we would still go to Arizona. We loaded up the family station wagon and our airstream trailer. Besides my mom and us kids, I think that trailer was my dad's prized possession. [laughs]

Looking back at it, did anything seem unusual at the time?

Nothing, nothing at all. We had been making this trip every year since I was a baby. We always took the same road and camped out at the same location. We wouldn't stay at any campground because those cost money. Instead, Dad always took us into the desert. He had a very particular spot that he deemed the "perfect exploring spot." The spot was off one of the main roads and only 5 miles away from the nearest gas station. So we were out in nature, but we were also close enough to civilization if we needed anything. I remember the ride down being just like any other. My brother David was playing with his action figures in the backseat and trying, but failing, to not to pay any attention to me. I was just six years old and still didn't under-stand a few things, like telling a joke. I understood that people said they had a joke to tell and then people would laugh afterwards, but I didn't understand the actual concept of a joke. So every couple of minutes or so, I would try to get my brother David's attention and tell him, "David, let me tell you a joke," and then I would proceed to laugh maniacally like I had just told him the greatest joke in the world. He was pretty understanding about this at first, but after a couple of hours, he very politely told me to shut up. I didn't listen...

Did you have any indication that the US government had been conducting nuclear tests not far from where your family camped?

No. At least I didn't. And by the time we started camping there, those tests had long been done with. I don't think my parents really worried about it either. It was the 50s, after all. Everyone still trusted the government. Why would they put the wrong people at risk? I can say for me personally we never noticed anything abnormal, even when we ventured far away from our campsite. It just looked like a normal desert. So, when we got to our campsite, we did the usual thing. We set up the trailer, then Mom started cooking dinner while Dad set up the campsite. Me and David helped them for a little bit, and then went on to play around the campsite.

When did things start to seem out of the ordinary?

A little into the afternoon. I remember me and David were playing around with echoes. You know, when you scream really loud into a cavern to see how your voice carries. Well, after doing this a few times, we heard a noise back.

Do you remember what it sounded like?

It sounded like a mix between a rattlesnake's rattle and a cicada's buzzing, you know, that loud bug you always hear in the summertime. We ran to Dad for safety, thinking it was a small herd of rattlesnakes coming to get us. My parents weren't quite sure what was making the noise either, but my father grabbed his shotgun just to be on the safe side. My father was not what you would call a hunter. I myself had only seen him fire it a handful of times and even then, it was only against snakes or other pests around our property. He loaded up his gun and had me and my brother stand by our mom while he walked out towards the noise. The buzzing sounded like it was getting louder and louder until finally, Dad fired his gun into the air. I'm guessing this was an attempt to scare off whatever was out there. It worked though because as soon as we heard the gunshot, the rattling noise seemed to disappear. We weren't allowed to play far away from the trailer after that, just in case ended up being a snake or some other predator out there after all.

Was that the last time you heard it?

No. The next time we heard it was later that night when the actual attack happened. That night, we celebrated our first night of camping like we did every other night, with s'mores and some stargazing. The fire was going and we were listening to Dad name all of the constellations. He would tell us the meaning behind each and every one of them. He was telling us the story of Artemis when we started to hear that buzzing sound again. It sounded far away at first and seemed to be coming from the same direction as earlier. Dad stood up as soon as he heard it and stared into the darkness. The noise started to get closer and louder, and eventually, it sounded like it was coming from multiple directions. Dad put out the fire and rushed us all inside. Mom grabbed us kids and put us into the bedroom. She had us hide under the bed while she stayed in the room with us. She was too big to hide, but we were crying and screaming for her not to leave. I remember she was trying to calm us down and get us to be quiet, but when you're a kid, you don't under-stand the need for silence, especially when you are scared and hysterical. Our father had his gun in hand and was ducking down towards the front door of the trailer. I think that he was trying to avoid being seen by whatever might be out there. That's why, I'm guessing, he put out the fire, so that whatever animal it was would leave us alone. Had it been a normal animal, I'm sure that would have worked.

That buzzing sound was so loud at this point, I remember it was hurting my ears. I wasn't even as afraid as I once was, as much as I just wanted the noise to stop. And then it suddenly did. I remember seeing my dad's face after the noise stopped. He looked so confused and was still very alarmed, you could tell. He started to stand up slowly, still pointing his gun at the camper door. He looked out the window and then looked to my mother.

"What do you see?" she whispered.

"Nothing," Dad said. "I think they're gone. You and the kids stay here, I'm going to start the truck."

At that moment, the trailer wall behind Dad came crashing in. Two large mandibles came crashing through the wall first, followed by the rest of the creature's face. Of course, I would later find out that it was some sort of giant insects, but at the time, I remember thinking it was the bogeyman. I closed my eyes and cried hysterically as we heard my father scream and plead for mercy. The buzzing had started again and much to our horror, the trailer walls were now being hit from all sides. Mom was yelling for us to stay put as she ran after my father. I remember trying to hold on to David, but he was too scared and just wanted my mother. He went crawling out after her. I was holding on so tightly to him, I must've scratched his leg in the process, but he was still able to get loose. I heard my mother and David scream, and then I heard nothing but the buzzing. The back of the trailer had been ripped open where I was hiding. I stayed under the bed and tried to keep as still as possible. I remember I even covered my face and held my breath so that these things wouldn't know I was under the bed. I kept my eyes closed through most of this, only opening them once I felt one of the insects were close by. I remember squeezing my doll as hard as I could in an attempt to keep myself calm. I couldn't see much from under the bed, but I did see large insect legs and antenna searching the trailer. One of the bugs found my mother's sugar cubes in the kitchen pantry and then they all seemed to swarm towards that.

I waited under that bed for the next 12 hours. Even after the creatures were long gone, I was too afraid to move. I just remember squeezing my doll and reciting the Lord's Prayer. At some point, I feel asleep, but I'm not sure when. Eventually, I woke up to the noise of an airplane flying overhead. I don't remember much after that. I know the police found me wandering away from the trailer. They had received a call from the airplane pilot who saw my family's motorhome in tatters. The police officers were trying to ask me questions, but I was still in shock. Of course, this attack was a sign of things to come, but at the time, police were absolutely baffled. They got me the appropriate medical attention and thanks to the specialists, I was eventually able to talk again. Of course, it was some time before I was able to recount any of the events that took place...that night. [**Margaret seems to trail off as she notices a small bug climb up onto the patio table.**]

Margaret, are you okay?

I'm fine, dear, thank you...

These bugs are such pests this time of year. Now, where was I?

Oh yes, after spending some time in therapy, I was eventually released to my grandparents, who lived in Utah. The whole situation was kept very hush-hush for a little while. The government didn't want people to know that it may have created a monster. [**Margaret slams her hand down on the table, crushing the bug that was making its way to the sandwiches. She does not break eye contact with me the entire time.**] Eventually, I went back to school and then onto college, where I met my husband and we have spent the last 40 years here. It wasn't until I was in my 30s that my attack was made public knowledge and at that point, I was thankfully stable enough to answer whatever questions the press had for me. Since my husband passed a few years back, I am content with spending my time with my grandchildren.

[Margaret waves to her two grandsons, who wave back. It is only then that I realize the boys are playing with a magnifying glass.]

"What are you doing, boys?" Margaret asks.

"Killing ants, Nana," says the grandson with the magnifying glass.

"Good," Margaret replies. She begins to pick off the insect pieces on her palm and smiles.

WENDIGO

Quebec, Canada

The icy streets of Quebec are proving hard to navigate. I have been to plenty of exotic places during my interviews, but none so as unique as Quebec. My interview is with Bryan Condit, known best as the only survivor of the Wendigo attack. In the winter of 1982, a severe blizzard hit the small town of Georgetown in the Prince Edward Island district of Canada. Whether the Wendigo created the storm or not is still debated, but what is known is that this monstrosity wiped out the entire population of Georgetown, with the exception of Bryan. Now, Bryan has graciously agreed to tell his story, in hopes that it can one day help others.

It was cold that winter. I mean, it is always cold, it is Canada after all, but that winter specifically was very rough. School didn't get canceled much in those days, the snow was just something that you were expected to deal with, but they canceled it the day before the blizzard. This was great news to my sister Josephine and I. We didn't mind the cold and we certainly loved playing in the snow. The blizzard made no difference to us.

How old were you?

I was 14. My sister Josephine was 11 going on 30. We loved the snow. Our whole family was what you would call outdoorsmen. My parents were both ex-military. Once they found out they were pregnant with me, they finished up their time in the service and moved us farther north. Dad found work with an insurance agency and my mother became a schoolteacher.

Why did they decide to move so far north? To be closer to family?

My father didn't talk to his family, and my mother's family is the reason that she joined the military to begin with. No, we moved further north to get away from it all. My father, you see, he had a mentality of prepare for the worst and hope for the best. Me, I just used to think that he was paranoid.

Did he settle down once you got to Georgetown?

My father never settled. [laughs] We were still too close to the water for his liking, but we were also far enough away from any nuclear power plants, so I think it was a risk that he felt was worth taking. Regardless of how things played out, I think if I were in my father's situation, I would have done the exact same thing. Once we got to Georgetown, my parents bought a small plot of land and began building our house. My father built the house and bunker at the same time. He did this, I think, to avoid suspicion. If anything, our neighbors thought that we were just going to have a large basement. This may seem like overkill in a lot of ways, but my father wanted our bunker to be a secret. In case the worst should ever happen, he didn't want anyone to be able to break into our shelter.

Tell me about the blizzard.

Well, we knew it was coming for the last few weeks. Like I said, it had been a particularly bad winter that year so none of us were too surprised when it happened. The blizzard started on a Wednesday night, I believe. Josephine and I woke up to a snow day and played in the backyard with our dog Genghis. My mother graded papers inside while Dad tested the generator. He wanted to be prepared in case we lost power. Everything seemed fairly normal that first day. It was not until the early hours of the next morning that things started to go horribly wrong. I remember waking up to Genghis growling at the window. I slept on the second floor of our house, right across from my parents' room. Genghis slept with me every single night. Even though I wasn't supposed to, I let him sleep on the bed. Genghis was a hunting dog, he didn't get spooked by much, so I knew it was serious. As I got up to see what he was growling at, I immediately heard a large boom come from outside. I'm not sure what caused that noise, even to this day, but I know that whatever it was was close enough to shake the house. My father raced into my room to check on me. Once he saw that I was okay, he looked out the window. I'm not sure exactly what he saw, but all it took was one look. He yelled to my mother to grab my sister and told me to grab my jacket. "We're going to the shelter," he said.

At what point did you realize it was a Kaiju attack?

Not until we were inside the shelter. We had cameras set up around the house. Once we got underground, my father went to the room that he called the "command center." In the command center, he had set up a live feed to our house cameras. This way, he was able to look around our house and try and get a better view of what was going on. The way he was acting, I think he thought we were under attack by terrorists maybe. Looking back, I would have gladly taken terrorists over the monster.

All of us followed Dad into the command center. At first, we couldn't see anything. The blizzard was still very strong and made it difficult to discern what was smoke and what was snow. The quality of camera that was available back in those days was also not the best. There were only six cameras. One for each side of the house, one for the garage, and one for the front door. We were all scanning the cameras, going back-and-forth between the screens, when we finally saw it by the garage camera. We got a clear view of our driveway and our street. We saw some neighbors running, I'm still not sure which ones, but they looked terrified. They were going from house to house trying to get someone to let them in. It was only a few seconds before we saw the creature come into frame behind them. Even with the low-quality of camera and the limited visibility, we saw plenty. The Kaiju was covered in fur and walking on all fours. It would've almost looked like a wolf if not for its skeletal face and horns. We had seen reports of Kaiju in the news, but those creatures resembled reptiles or insects. Besides, those attacks always took place in southern climates. Not this far north, and certainly not in the winter.

What did you do after seeing it?

Me? I didn't do anything. I was shocked and frozen with utter disbelief. My mom and dad, on the other hand, were quick to action. We were taken out of the command center so that we didn't see what happened to the neighbors. My mom began to check the shelter and take inventory of everything. We weren't sure how long we were going to be down there. One thing was certain, as long as that creature was aboveground, we were staying below. My father stayed in the command center for the next three hours. We hardly slept at all that first night. Even though we were underground, we could still hear quite a bit of what was going on up there. We heard a lot of screams and cries for help. Occasionally, we would hear the sound of a nearby house being destroyed or what sounded like a car being crushed. None of those noises compared to the howls of the monster itself. It didn't sound quite like a wolf howl, it sounded almost like a cackle, like that of a hyena. It sounded like the creature was howling with laughter. This laughter, along with its skeletal appearance, is why the press has since dubbed the creature Wendigo.

When did the power get cut?

I'm not sure on the exact time, but I know it was fairly early into Wendigo's attack. At some point, the creature destroyed the power-lines using a car or some other large object. Of course, this didn't affect us too bad thanks to all of the generators that we had. We used them for only space heaters and lights. The cameras went out with the power. So we were hiding out in the dark from what was going on up top.

Did you have any way to communicate with the outside world?

No. We had walkie-talkies that we could with each other, but that was it. We did have an emergency broadcast radio but had no luck with it. Whether that was because of the storm or Wendigo, I am not sure.

How long were you down there then?

We were underground for almost 5 days. My parents really held us together during that time. Dad would give us some busywork to keep our minds off things. He would have us do homework while we were down there. Given the choice between my teachers and my father, I think I much preferred my teachers. Even during a time of crisis, our father would still be the disciplinarian. He issued us tests in math and science that he had made up himself. If we missed a question, he would make us do exercises. Every missed question was 25 pushups, sit-ups, or my personal favorite, burpees. My mother wasn't nearly as harsh. She kept us busy by having us play board games and cards. Some nights, she would read to us just like when we were younger. She would have a unique voice for every single character in the story. Even at 14 years old and in the presence of utter horror, Mom could still make us feel like all was right in the world.

What happened on the fifth day?

In the early morning of that fifth day is when the Wendigo finally found our family. It had been a few days since we heard anything above ground and since we did not have the ability to use our cameras, my father decided he would be the one to leave the shelter and see if the creature had moved on. We waited for him for what felt like hours, when in reality, it could not of been more than 20 minutes. When he finally returned, he looked absolutely terrified. During my 14 years of life, the only emotion my father showed was a constant scowl. He would occasionally smile when talking to us kids or my mother, but for the most part, he was a very serious man. When he returned, I saw something I had never seen on my father's face. I saw fear. Once he finally got all of his gear off, he told us that he did not see any signs of life in the town. He had not gone far from our shelter but given the fact we lived so close to the town, he did not need to. He didn't give us the gory details, but he made it clear that it did not look like there had been any survivors.

What about Wendigo?

Dad said that he did not see the creature, but was worried it was still near. He said that as he was sneaking through the town, he was able to see a trail of blood leading from the town to the forest. At first, he thought that the creature had found some unfortunate soul and had dragged them into the woods for a snack. However, shortly after finding this trail, my father heard what he described as a dying animal. He believed that somehow, Wendigo had either been injured somehow or eaten something that was causing it to get sick. Regardless, my father decided to come back to the shelter. That is when him and my mother began to plan our next move. The plan was that we were going to give it another three days. If we did not hear anything up top then Dad was going to go back topside in an attempt to find help in Melbourne, the next town over. Even if Wendigo wasn't dying in the woods, we hoped that this would be enough time for it to become bored and move on to another location.

But it didn't take three days?

No, it only took a few hours after that. It was nighttime when we woke to Genghis, who was growling at the shelter door, his hair standing on edge. I whispered Genghis's name to get him to come to me, but when I did, we were all awoken to a loud banging against the shelter door. I'll never know how Wendigo found us, if she saw my father when he was sneaking through the town or if she caught his scent somehow and tracked him back to our shelter. Either way, she had found us and she wanted inside. The shelter wasn't attached directly to our house. There was an entrance through our garage, which we kept well hidden. There was also a back entrance to the backyard that we could use if anything happened to the front entrance. Of course, none of our defenses were capable of stopping this creature from getting in.

We knew Wendigo was too big to get into our shelter, but she was still able to break the door down. She busted through the metal door like it was nothing. At first, she was only being able to fit her mouth and teeth through the small opening. It was so loud. The creature was making all sorts of unnatural noises, Genghis was barking, and my father was yelling out orders like he was a four-star general. He told my mother to grab the bag and for me and my sister to follow her. He grabbed the gasoline that had been powering the generator and began to pour it all over the inside of the shelter. Wendigo was getting further and further into the shelter. This thing was very determined, scratching and clawing its way through the foundation. It wanted us, and it was going to get to us no matter what. I got a glimpse of its face as we were running away. Although its body resembled that of a wolf, its face looked like a skull. The skin on its face was very tight against the skull. The taut skin even covered the eye holes of the creature, giving it even more of a deformed look.

We made our way towards the exit with my father right behind us. Although I did not see it, I am guessing that he lit a match and threw it into the shelter, because the last thing I remember was feeling the heat at my back as my mother rushed us outside. My father and Genghis were right behind us. As we started to stand up, my father was slamming the shelter door shut. We heard Wendigo squeal in pain as it was burnt alive. In its ravenous attempt to get into our shelter, the Wendigo had gotten stuck in the entrance. As we made our way out of the backyard, we could see the back half of the creature writhing in pain as the flames consumed it.

So it was over? You all made it out okay?

We made it out, but it was not over. We were now out in the open, exposed to the elements. Wendigo had destroyed most of the town, leaving us with no options for shelter. We had almost no resources except for what was in our travel bag. There was still a blizzard, although I will admit it was not nearly as bad as what it had been the days prior. To make matters worse, we were all in our pajamas. Our cold-weather gear was burning with the Wendigo. Realizing that our options and time was limited, our parents elected to travel to the next town, which was only five miles away. We looted some winter jackets, snow boots, and guns from what was left of the Wendigo's victims and began our journey to Melbourne. We didn't find much in the way of firepower besides a shotgun and a couple of handguns, but it was enough for our small family. All other weapons we found either had no ammunition or looked to have been partially digested.

Georgetown and Melbourne were only separated by five miles of forest area. It was quicker to cut through the woods, instead of walking the ten miles along the road. This route also kept us safe from wind chill as opposed to the other paths that left us exposed. Dad had his rifle on hand should we encounter any wildlife. Of course, that didn't end up helping much...

We could not have been walking for more then 20, 30 minutes when Dad suddenly stopped. Genghis stopped with him and instantly started to growl again. Armed with only a couple torches, our visibility was still very limited at night, but we could hear something. It was in front of us, but it didn't sound too big. We had stopped dead in our tracks for what I was praying to be nothing more than a raccoon. We started to hear more movement. This time, the noise was coming from all around us. Whatever was out there was surrounding us. At first, we thought it could possibly be a pack of wolves, but then we heard it. That familiar cackle of the Wendigo. Of course, now we know that the Wendigo was pregnant and that those pain-filled noises my father heard were the sounds of her in labor. I am guessing she attacked our shelter in order to feed us to her babies. Now, in some cruel twist of fate, we brought ourselves to their dinner table.

Once we realized that we were surrounded, we began to form a tight circle around each other. Dad urged us not to fire at anything unless we were sure we had a shot. He did not want us to panic and waste our bullets at the darkness. For a few seconds, we were at a standoff with the creatures. Neither one of us wanted to make the first move, until finally out of the darkness came a skeletal face towards my father. He fired at it just in time and the demonic pup went down, but that was all the invitation the others needed to start the attack.

I still don't know how many there were, but it felt like hundreds. Despite my father's urgings, I was firing my gun at anything that was in front of me. In the frenzy, one of the pups charged me. He hit me so hard in the side that the wind was knocked out of me as I landed. That is when I saw the Wendigo pup over top of me. It opened its mouth, ready to claim its prize, when Genghis suddenly jumped on top of it, biting into its neck. The Wendigo and Genghis rolled on the ground, biting and nipping at each other. Neither one seemed to have a clear advantage until my sister finally shot the Wendigo. She hit it right between the eyes. She reached out her hand, helping me stand up. As she told me to be more careful, I saw another skeletal pup attack her from behind, catching her off guard. She screamed wildly for help as the creature ripped into her. My parents turned their attention from the pack of monsters surrounding us to her. Dad swung his rifle like a baseball bat into the creature. He hit it with all the force he could muster. I heard the creature's bones break more and more with every hit. After what seemed like a couple hundred hits, the pup released Josephine. Once it was off of her, Mom fired at the creature, killing it. I was yelling for help for Josephine as I started to bandage her up. But by then, it was too late. The creatures, seizing their opportunity, were swarming at us now like a ravenous plague. Their sick cackle could be heard the entire time. I remember hearing my mother scream in pain as two of the monsters charged her, each one attacking her limbs. My sister was being dragged away from us and into the darkness by another two pack members. I was hysterical, trying to find my gun so that I could shoot at anything, but once I finally did and I pulled the trigger, nothing happened. I had spent all my bullets. Worst of all, I could no longer see my mother or my sister. I could only hear their cries for help, and then nothing. My father, having just dispatched the other pack members, was now running wildly towards where my mother and sister have been dragged off, screaming for them as he ran but not hearing anything except the silence of the forest...

All the strength my father had seemed to be gone in that instant. He looked like he had just lost his entire world. He just collapsed to his knees in disbelief. I called for him a few times to ask what we should do next. He didn't answer for a little while, before turning his attention to me and my wounds. My leg had been badly bitten and the back of my neck and head was pretty scratched up. Dad began to bandage me up and told me to watch the trees for any movement. Whatever ammunition we found in town had been used up during that initial attack. Faced with the cold and the danger of predators, we had to keep moving, but my leg and the amount of blood lost made that very difficult. Dad had also suffered some injuries but for the most part appeared to be okay. I urged my father to go after Mom and Josephine, but he silenced me as soon as I brought it up. With tears in his eyes, he looked at me and said two words I will never forget. "They're gone."

It was not long after this attack that we heard the cackle of the pack again. I was feeling lightheaded due to the amount of blood I was losing. I wasn't sure how much longer I could keep fighting. They didn't attempt to surround us this time. They knew we were wounded and I expect thought they could overwhelm us with their sheer numbers. We saw the remaining pack members start to get closer, charging full speed towards us. I don't know what came over me, maybe it was the loss of my sister and mother or just the utter hopelessness of the situation, but I was pissed. I steadied myself with the baseball bat I had in hand and saw them charging out of the darkness once more. I let out a loud, almost inhuman scream, and began to swing wildly at the beasts. Everything was so chaotic. I remember hearing screams, but I don't know if they were coming from us or the pups. Genghis had a pup by the throat and Dad was whacking the hell out of them with the butt of his rifle. Everything else was just a blur of rage and survival. At some point, I remember my vision getting blurry and I collapsed. The blood loss had been too much for me. I remember hearing my father scream like a madman as I succumbed to the darkness.

But you did survive.

Only because of my family. I woke three days later in the Melbourne doctor's office with Genghis laying at the foot of the bed. Even the medical staff couldn't keep him from me. Poor guy had suffered some pretty serious scratches and even lost an eye, but he was alive.

And your father?

My father killed every single one of those creatures that night...

He then somehow carried me the rest of the way to Melbourne, where he found some people walking near the tree line. He collapsed shortly after that, finally giving in to his wounds. The doctors were able to save my leg, but I was never able to walk quite the same way. After we recovered, me and Genghis went on to live with my aunt and uncle in Quebec, and I have been here ever since. Besides needing a cane to walk around, I am lucky. I just wish my family could have made it out with me. Georgetown was eventually rebuilt. They wanted me to be a part of the ceremony commemorating the new town, but I just couldn't do it. I only pray that no one has to go through anything like what my family experienced that horrible night. More importantly, I hope that KRSD will do everything in their power to make sure that never happens again.

RUGABA

Ann Arbor, Michigan

These interviews do not typically allow me to sit down with other KRSD field operatives like myself and discuss our unique experiences, which is why I'm grateful to be sitting with Mr. Stephen Brinkman. Mr. Brinkman has been a KRSD field operative for the last 18 years. His assignments have taken him all over the world to examine the aftereffects of reported Kaiju attacks. It is Stephen's job to document and record these incidents to allow the KRSD to confirm the attacks as being Kaiju in nature.

It was much different 10 years ago. We didn't have the team of researchers or security detail that we do now. Back then, if there were reports of a Kaiju attack, they would only send a small team of 3 to 5 people to investigate. Because of the regular occurrence of these things are showing up now, we have teams scattered throughout the globe. This, along with the teams back at headquarters that would be on a chopper and en route to whatever location they are given within a matter of hours. Whenever there was a reported attack, we'd send these small teams to investigate. Back in the day, it wasn't uncommon to not hear from some research teams for up to two months at a time. Sometimes, we would have to send new research teams just to check on the old ones. Most of the time, the teams were fine. They had just forgot to check in. Sometimes though, something had led to the death of one or all of the team members.

Were you ever a part of those missions? The ones to check on other field operatives?

Oh yes, many times, but only one time did we come face-to-face with something peculiar. It was roughly 8 years ago in the northern region of Uganda. A team assigned to that region hadn't checked in for the last month, even missing their rendezvous with their travel guides. They had been investigating a possible Kaiju attack in that region. It appeared that something was killing whole herds of animals. It mostly focused on zebra and caribou, but this most recent report was that it had taken out an entire family of elephants. To make matters worse, this thing had started attacking villages. Officials worried that it would start growing more bold and attack a majorly populated area soon.

It sounds like a Kaiju to me...

You would think so, but until the KRSD can confirm that it is an actual Kaiju and not some overly aggressive animal then the United Nations won't help. Of course, they don't always need us to confirm the presence of a Kaiju. A rampaging hundred-foot-tall dinosaur walking down Main Street is proof enough. In cases like these, however, where much of the area is still rural and predators are aplenty, then they bring us in to investigate. Most the time, we are just looking for rudimentary things like footprints or taking samples in the soil to test for radiation. In a case like the one in Northern Uganda, we would also look at the remains of the animals that were attacked, but unfortunately, it is an area full of predators. Whatever proof was on these remains was usually picked clean by the hyenas, vultures, and lions. Now, the villages being attacked were a different story altogether.

Three villages had been attacked, leaving only a few survivors. Most of them rambled on about some demon that had come from the water to attack their village. The United Nations was quick to point out that most of these villages were right next to the river, meaning that they could've been damaged by the river itself or the many predators within it—hippos, crocodiles, etcetera. This is why they needed us to verify it was a Kaiju.

The team disappearing in the area wasn't confirmation enough?

No, unfortunately, it was not...

The official reason the United Nations gave us was that due to the complexity of the region, they had no way of knowing what had caused these previous issues or the disappearance of our team, and if they were even related. Of course, I like the unofficial reason that I was given by my team lead, which was, "It's fucking Africa. There are lions and rebels and shit, and everything is trying to kill you." I myself think that he watched a few too many reruns on Animal Planet, but he did have a point. The area was dangerous. At that point in time, the general region was having some issues with a few small rival factions. It was entirely possible that the previous KRSD team met an unfortunate end at the hands of some rebel forces. I personally think it was highly unlikely, though. Whatever this creature was, it was affecting the safety of every person in the region, including the rebels. They wanted this thing gone as much as the rest of us, so it was unlikely to me that they would have done anything to the team responsible for giving them aid, but what do I know? I just chased giant fucking monsters for a living.

Can you tell me about the actual expedition itself?

Right, sorry, I can get off topic pretty quick. The actual expedition itself started out fairly simple. All we had to do was retrace the previous team's steps. To do this, we did everything that they did. We started by recruiting a guide to help us. He was a local man named Machupa, and if the stories were to be believed, then we were in pretty good hands.

What stories?

Supposedly, he was a big thorn in the side for some of the rebel groups. As the story goes, when Machupa's village was attacked, he led a few of the villagers against the much better-armed rebels and put a boot in their ass. Spending just a little bit of time with him, it was pretty clear that Machupa was a man that you could rely on. He had a vast knowledge about the area, was fluent in the native tongue, and had a personal stake in the matter as well. I guess his friend was the guide for the original team of KRSD researchers. So we had an expert guide and tracker, a handsome field researcher, one of the KRSD's best zoologists in Dr. Kendra Dietz, our field medic Dr. James Comstock, and for added muscle, we had Marine Mike.

Is Marine Mike his full name?

That's the name I was given. I don't know much about him besides the fact that his name was Mike, he was in the Marines, he loves big guns, loose women, drinks like a fish, and swears like a pirate. He's a nice guy, has a horrible drinking habit, but a nice guy. Between him and Machupa though, we were in pretty good hands.

We took a plane into the Ugandan territory and then met up with Machupa, who then drove us along the same route of the previous team. We stopped along the way at a small village that Machupa said was attacked the night prior to our arrival. We inspected the damage around the village as well as the remains of some villagers. Seeing things up close and personal, it was pretty clear that there was a Kaiju problem here. The tracks that were left over from the previous attacks were reptile in nature and triple the size of any known predators in that area. Honestly, I think we had everything we needed from that initial visit, but we were determined to at least try and find some trace of the previous team. We owed that much to them to at least try and find out what happened.

We stayed in the village that night. We figured it was unlikely that the creature would return two nights in a row when it had picked the area clean already. Dr. Comstock was administering aid to the villagers while the rest of us checked our equipment and tried to help out however we could. I remember one woman holding the remains of her son and crying hysterically as the other women around her kept wailing out the same words over and over again. "Rugaba, Rugaba, Rugaba," they kept saying. I remember there was something almost supernatural about it, like they were praying to and cursing something all at the same time. The next day, as we began our journey, I asked Muchapa what Rugaba meant. "Rugaba is the god of judgement," he said. According to Machupa, the women in the village were praying for him to avenge their loved ones. "These attacks have led to a lot of prayer to many different gods, but so far, no action."

We drove out to the last reported location of the KRSD team, which was a small camping outpost at the edge of the jungle. The team would go out during the day to conduct field tests and would usually return the same night. It had been a total of three weeks since the last person had seen our team members. We ventured into the jungle with Machupa leading the way. The thing I remember most about the jungle is how silent it was. Usually, these types of ecosystems are crawling with all sorts of creatures. Hell, even the bugs make a lot of noise, but not this time. This area was very quiet. This trend continued for the next couple hours as we went deeper and deeper into the jungle. We were fairly confident that there was a Kaiju in the area, so we weren't looking to travel too far. We were just searching for some sort of sign of our team members or definitive proof for the United Nations that hopefully didn't involve one of us being eaten alive.

An hour into our journey, Machupa raised his hand in the air signaling for us to halt. He began to look around while Mike slowly raised his gun. We stood still for what seemed like an eternity but couldn't have been more than a few seconds. All of us were looking around wildly into the bush, trying to see any indication of something coming towards us. Machupa finally lowered his hand, and the tension of the group with it. Mike began to lower his weapon when suddenly, we heard a disturbance coming from our side. I'm not sure if I started running before I heard Machupa yell or after, all I know is that I was going as fast as I could towards the opposite end of whatever was making that noise in the brush. I heard a lot of noises during the next few seconds, but mostly a lot of yelling and gunfire. I kept running until the ground disappeared in front of me and I began to fall forward into the brush. When I lifted myself up, I was covered in mud and knee-deep in water. Apparently, I had ran all the way to a nearby lagoon. I wasn't alone though, as the rest of the group was beside me in the mud and shit. We didn't have time to think though, as the brush around the lagoon start to shake again. I remember thinking, "this is it, we're fucked," when suddenly a family of gazelles came out from the brush and began to drink from the lagoon. We all started to nervously laugh as we realized the identity of our would-be attackers. It was a good long and loud laugh that was definitely needed after all of the turmoil we had just faced.

We started to discuss turning back, sure of the fact that we had all of the confirmation we needed for the United Nations. We began gathering our things that were strung about the lagoon when I saw a KRSD field bag. I had assumed it belonged to Dr. Kendra, but when I tried to hand it to her, she assured me that she still had hers. We then looked at the name on the bag and found it belonged to a Dr. Samuel Runghammer, one of the members of the previous team.

Did you find anything else from the previous team?

[Stephen grimaces.] We found...what was left...of the previous team. Let me put it this way. We found enough of the previous team's gear and...remains to, without a shadow of a doubt, verify this was a Kaiju attack.

What happened then?

What happened then? What happened is that we started to get the fuck out of there before the Kaiju came back to its nest. We gathered our supplies and what little remains were left and started back towards the campsite. We actually got fairly close to it to before we started to hear the noises. I think they would've sounded pretty common if it hadn't been for the screams attached to them.

At some point between us arriving to the camp and returning, it appears the Kaiju had attacked the campsite. That is when we got our first view of this monster. This thing had the face of an crocodile but was able to walk on two legs. At a distance, it would've been easy to confuse it with a dinosaur. It couldn't've been more than 50 feet tall. As soon as it saw us emerge from the brush, its gaze was focused on us. Mike and Machupa started yelling for us to get down as they started to fire at the creature. We obliged them, ducking into the brush and watching in horror as the bullets seemed to bounce off the hide of this thing. Mike and Machupa fired until there was nothing left. As soon as the barrage of gunfire ended, the creature stood up, blood still dripping from its mouth. Collectively, we began to back up towards the tree line. It's funny how even the most hardened of individuals can turn to absolute mush, given the right circumstances. All of us were well-trained individuals—hell, Mike and Machupa were even battle-hardened veterans—but in that instant, we were all dreading the blood-drenched Kaiju in front of us, at least until the other Kaiju showed up.

The other Kaiju?

Yes. I had heard reports of Kaiju fighting each other in the wild but had never seen it in person. We backed into the trees, awaiting our fate, wondering which of us the Kaiju would attack first. The creature began to approach us when suddenly it stopped, its gaze fixated on something else, something above the trees. I looked up as I felt a large shadow looming over top of me and was absolutely frozen in fear. Behind us stood another Kaiju. This one with the head of an elephant and standing almost 100 feet tall. He had piercing black eyes, and his body was covered in spikes. The thing that stood out the most about him were his tusks, which each had countless miniature tusks protruding from them, almost like thorns. This Kaiju was almost twice the size of the one in front of us. No matter how I saw it, we were fucked.

The Kaiju at our backs took two steps forward so that he was standing between us and the crocodile Kaiju. There was a long silence after that as the crocodile was visibly perplexed, trying to decide his next move. He wasn't the only one, as the rest of us just watched in confusion as this elephant Kaiju had come to our aid. Just then, the crocodile Kaiju seemingly made his decision, as he let out a sickening roar that made us all, even Mike, wince in terror. The elephant Kaiju matched his roar with a sound of his own. Something about this moment was very profound for me and won't be something I'm likely to ever forget. Hearing these creatures roar at one another snapped me into a state of mind I've never been in before. No longer was I Stephen Brinkman, handsome KRSD field operative. I was transported back to a different, more primal time, like I had experienced this before on some genetic level. These things made me feel very helpless. All my success, all my being, was nothing in that moment. I was nothing. It was a mix of fear and admiration that I have yet to ever come close to experiencing in life since.

What happened next was nothing short of absolute primal aggression as the two Kaiju lurched towards each other with savage speed. The crocodile creature was clawing at our elephant savior as he began to grapple with the beast. Once the elephant had a hold of it, he began punching the creature with all of his might. Each punch sounded like a rumble of thunder as the crocodile eventually went limp. The elephant Kaiju threw him across the plains like he was nothing. The crocodile, realizing he had more then met his match, began to scurry towards the opposite tree line in a panicked attempt to escape his fate, but it wasn't enough. The elephant Kaiju grabbed the other by the tail, pulling him back. He then grabbed the crocodile's jaws and began to twist. Try as he might, the crocodile couldn't escape his fate as the elephant twisted his head clean off of his body, letting out a victorious roar as he held his trophy within his grasp. Just like that, the battle was over. The surviving Kaiju began lumbering towards the bush, paying little to no attention to us as he left. A sudden mist had overtaken the jungle, concealing him as he went on his way until there was nothing left except a sudden rainfall.

It was a few minutes before I was finally able to speak again, but when I finally regained the gift of gab, I asked something to the extent of, "What in the holy fuck of all mankind was that thing?"

Machupa let out a small laugh of relief as he looked to the sky and answered, "Rugaba."

Of course, when we returned, we had all of the proof we needed for a UN-funded Kaiju expedition, but they didn't end up finding anything. The area had no more strange reports of Kaiju, other than a select few reports of some elephant monster terrorizing some poachers, but I'm sure that was just the local superstition...

LIVING IN A WORLD OF MONSTERS

The emergence of the Kaiju has been a humbling experience for mankind, to say the least. Not only are we not the top of the food chain anymore, but now we face an enemy that could quite literally cause our extinction. We still don't know exactly what creates these monsters or even where they are coming from. What we do know is that the number of yearly Kaiju attacks has tripled in the last 20 years. Each major Kaiju that has emerged seems stronger than the last, and while we have been able to beat these creatures back so far, Doctor Iwata and her team at the KRSD fear we are on borrowed time.

These monsters are like a nightmare. It is no wonder why many people around the world think of Kaiju as God's punishment for our crimes against the Earth. The emergence of these creatures has forced mankind to drastically change our way of life. Water travel has become virtually extinct, with cruise ships and boating excursions a thing of the past. Companies are relying more and more on air travel to transport their cargo, using transport by cargo ship as an absolute last resort.

Because of the Kaiju's affinity for the sea, countries around the world have increased the sizes of their navies, so much so that military experts estimate the world's naval forces have increased nearly 10 times what they were at the end of World War II.

Coastal cities are feeling the most pressure from these attacks with many people and businesses moving inland and further north. To fight this, many coastal cities have begun taking extreme measures. States such as Texas and Florida have started building giant walls in an attempt to keep the Kaiju away from their cities. Other areas around the world are setting up nets and other defense systems around the coast to deter the Kaiju. Real estate around the world has also greatly changed, with many residential areas advertising Kaiju shelters as part of their sales pitch. Cities around the world are creating underground shelters for the residents to retreat to should one of these monsters get too close.

We have begun to depend more on our military forces since police, firefighters, and other first responders are severely unprepared to deal with such a threat. Because of this, many military bases have been created around the world for the rapid deployment of troops and artillery. The United Nations are working to establish a global precedent to deal with these creatures.

Unfortunately, even in these most dangerous of times, some countries are refusing to work together. This has led to a continued reliance on the men and women of the Kaiju Survival and Research Department (KRSD). The KRSD is made up of some of the brightest and most capable minds in the world. These professionals have devoted their lives to study of Kaiju in the field and learning everything they can about their origins, their biology, and their weaknesses. Many brave men and women died so that we could have the information that is in this guide, but even with all this information, it is still alarming how little researchers understand about the Kaiju.

After reading this guide, you should have a clear understanding of the dangerous situation mankind is in. Apply what you have learned into real-world scenarios. Whatever world mankind builds from here on out will be a direct result of your labor. It is only by working together that we have any hope of beating back these nightmarish creatures.

A MONSTER WORLD

KRSD scientists have put together two doomsday scenarios that they fear could lead to mankind's extinction. While we hope to never have to deal with one of these scenarios, let alone both of them, the possibility of them happening is very real.

THE KING OF THE MONSTERS

We have already covered the different categories of Kaiju in depth, so we will not go over them again, but any kind that is capable of firing nuclear energy is an obvious threat to any living organism on this planet. Should a Kaiju of this power ever emerge, it would be capable of wiping out whole cities in a single blast of energy. Destroying such a creature could possibly set off a nuclear blast that would take the lives of anyone within a few miles' radius. KRSD specialists hope that this creature remains just a nightmare and never becomes a reality. Unfortunately, due to the creatures' increased radioactive levels in the field and their continued evolutionary leaps, we fear that it is only a matter time before this nightmare comes true.

THE KING'S COURT

We are still not entirely sure just how intelligent the Kaiju are. From what we do understand, these monsters seem to have no social structure and do not play well with each other. This fact has worked to humanity's advantage as we typically only have to deal with one Kaiju attacking at a time. The few times in history that these monsters have attacked the same area has always ended in the two of them fighting each other for territory. This has always worked in the military's favor, allowing them to eliminate the two distracted targets with minimal resistance. However, KRSD researchers fear that this will not always be the case.

After watching these creatures closely in controlled environments, we have seen that they are capable of learning and problem-solving. Researchers worry that it is only a matter of time before they realize that their food source is also one of their greatest threats, and that they are capable of surviving much longer if they work together. While we have not seen this pack mentality develop to the extent that we see it in other animals, such as wolves or whales, this is still a concern to our researchers. One Kaiju is capable of destroying whole cities. Multiple Kaiju working together could destroy the human race in a matter of weeks. Should these creatures ever evolve enough to organize and attack as one, it would be the end of humankind as we know it.

THE FUTURE OF OUR WORLD

Should any of these scenarios take place, our time on this planet would be limited. Mankind would be forced to live in the shadows. Without the power of the world's military or our vast numbers and ability to organize, we can never hope to regain our planet. The world will give way to its new masters and the monsters will be unchallenged at the top of the food chain.

ABOUT THE ARTIST

The artwork in this Survival Guide is all thanks to the amazing José Lucas. He designed the beautiful cover art and KRSD logo. As a first time author, José was great to work with. If anything can be said about the book, its that the artwork is phenomenal. If you would like to contact José for your next book cover design, you can do so at https://www.facebook.com/stargazingstudio/

ABOUT THE AUTHOR

Wes Parker was born in Rochester Hills, MI. From the moment he could talk, Wes was telling stories. Whether it was to his mother, his friends, or the family dog, Wes just liked to tell stories. Today Wes spends his time writing these stories and adventuring with his beautiful wife Tiffany. Together they have two giant Labradors, who haven't quite realized they aren't lap dogs. The Kaiju Survival Guide is his debut novel

facebook.com/TheKaijuSurvivalGuide

twitter.com/MechaWes

Printed in Great Britain
by Amazon

46160089R10169